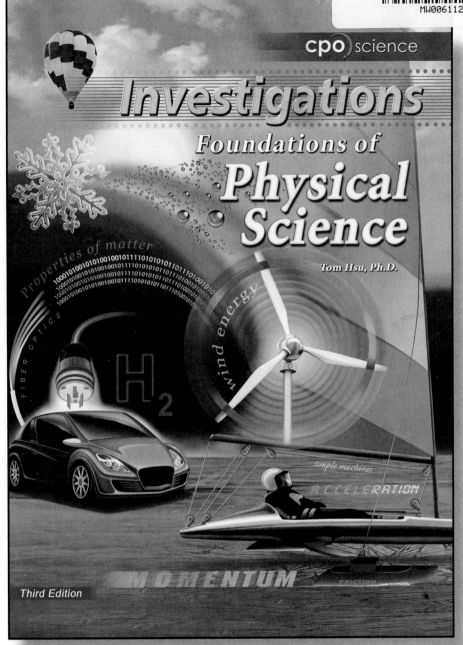

cpo science

Investigations

Foundations of
Physical
Science

Tom Hsu, Ph.D.

Properties of matter

FIBER OPTICS

H_2

wind energy

simple machines

ACCELERATION

MOMENTUM

FRICTION

Third Edition

cpo science

School Specialty®
Science

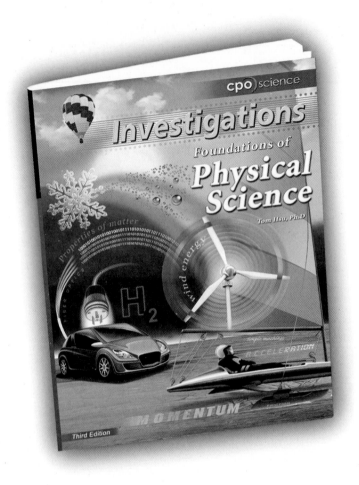

CPO Science *Foundations of Physical Science* Investigations
Third Edition

Copyright © 2018 CPO Science, a member of School Specialty Science
ISBN: 978-1-62571-829-7
Part Number: 1576084
Printing 2—April 2018
Printed by Webcrafters Inc., Madison, WI

CPO Science
80 Northwest Boulevard
Nashua, NH 03063
(866) 932-5227
http://www. cposcience.com

Printed and Bound in the United States of America

CREDITS

PRINCIPAL WRITERS

Thomas C. Hsu, PH.D – Author
Nationally recognized innovator in science and math education and the founder of CPO Science. Holds a Ph.D. in Applied Plasma Physics from the Massachusetts Institute of Technology (MIT), and has taught students from elementary, secondary and college levels. Tom has worked with numerous K–12 teachers and administrators and is well known as a consultant, workshop leader and developer of curriculum and equipment for inquiry based learning in science and math.

Erik Benton – Principal Investigation Editor and Writer
B.F.A., University of Massachusetts with minor in Physics
Taught for eight years in public and private schools, focusing on inquiry and experiential learning. Erik brings extensive teaching and technical expertise, ranging from elementary and adult education to wildlife research. As a naturalist for the Web of Life Field School in Santa Cruz, California, he participated in a worldwide amphibian population study. Currently he is involved in bird population studies in Massachusetts. Erik is our investigation writer and conducts national content presentations.

Scott Eddleman – Co-Author, Curriculum Manager
B.S., Biology, Southern Illinois University; M.Ed., Harvard University
Taught for 13 years in urban and rural settings. Developed two successful science-based school-to-career programs. Nationally recognized teacher trainer in inquiry-based and project-based instruction. Participated in a fellowship at Brown University where he conducted research on the coral reefs of Belize. Worked on National Science Foundation-funded projects at TERC. Scott has been a principal writer and curriculum developer for CPO Science for the last seven years.

Mary Beth Abel – Writer, Curriculum Specialist
B.S., Marine Biology, College of Charleston; M.S., Biological Sciences, University of Rhode Island.
Taught science and math at an innovative high school and at the college level. Has expertise in scientific research, inquiry-based teaching methods, and science curriculum development. Mary Beth has been a principal writer with CPO Science since 2000.

Patsy Eldridge – Writer
B.S., Biology, Grove City College; M.Ed., Tufts University.
Experienced science teacher and national hands-on science trainer and presenter. As an adjunct professor for Endicott College in Beverly, MA, and the College of Charleston, developed content-intensive Physical Science courses for educators. Partners with Dr. Tom Hsu to create and deliver innovative science lessons on interactive DVDs for students and teachers. Patsy has developed curriculum and training materials with CPO Science since 2000.

CONTRIBUTING WRITERS

Alyson Mazza
B.A., Environmental Biology and Education, Houghton College

Experienced science teacher with inquiry-based science teaching expertise. Alyson has worked with the PROBE K-12 project through the Leitzel Center at the University of New Hampshire to research and practice inquiry-based teaching strategies. She currently teaches science at Salem High School in Salem, NH.

Laura Preston
B. S. Geology and teaching certification, University of Texas, Arlington
Has thirteen years of science and math teaching experience for grades 5–12. Currently teaching at Salem High School in Salem, New Hampshire. Worked as a geologist in the early 1990's, and as a geophysicist in 2007. Laura participated in a research cruise aboard the R/V "Atlantis" collecting data on the East Pacific Rise. Member of the New Hampshire Geologic Society. Laura joined the CPO Science curriculum writing team as a consultant in 2007.

Michael Vela
Ph.D., Inorganic Chemistry, Brandeis University
Teaches 10th– and 11th–grade chemistry at Concord-Carlisle High School in Concord, Massachusetts. Taught 11th–grade chemistry at Lexington High School, Massachusetts.

Melissa Vela
B.A., Earth and Environmental Science, Lehigh University; M.S., Agricultural and Biological Engineering, Cornell University; M.Ed., Curriculum/Instruction, Boston College
Melissa has taught six years of 9th grade Earth and space science at Lexington High School in Massachusetts. She also taught 6th grade physical science and 8th grade algebra at Weston Middle School in Massachusetts.

SENIOR EDITOR

Lynda Pennell – Executive Vice President
B.A., English; M.Ed., Administration, Reading Disabilities, Northeastern University; CAGS Media, University of Massachusetts, Boston.
Nationally known in high school restructuring and for integrating academic and career education. Served as the director of an urban school for 5 years and has 17 years teaching/administrative experience in the Boston Public Schools. Lynda has led the development for CPO Science for the past eight years. She has also been recognized for her media production work.

EDITORIAL CONSULTANT

Christine Golden
B.A., Psychology, Gordon College: M.B.A., Rivier College
Project manager at *Imperial Communications* since 1999, with 22 years publishing experience. Owner and managing editor of *Big Dog Publishing Services*. Christine's work centers on editing of K-12 textbook material.

ART AND ILLUSTRATION

Polly Crisman – Graphics Manager/Illustration
B.F.A., University of New Hampshire
Worked as a designer and illustrator in marketing and advertising departments for a variety of industries. Polly has worked in the CPO Science design department since 2001, and is responsible for organizing workflow of graphics and file management. She created the CPO Science logo and supervises the graphic design image for CPO publications and media products.

Jesse Van Valkenburgh – Illustration/Photography
B.F.A. Illustration, Rochester Institute of Technology
Worked in prepress and design. Was responsible for creative design and prepress film production for computer catalogs, brochures and various marketing materials. Jesse completes photography and illustrations as a graphic designer for CPO book and media products.

Bruce Holloway – Senior Designer/Illustrator
Pratt Institute, N.Y., Boston Museum of Fine Arts
Expertise in illustration, advertising graphics, exhibits and product design. Commissioned throughout his career by The National Wildlife Federation's Conservation Stamp Campaign. Other commissions include the New Hampshire State Duck Stamp campaigns for1999 and 2003. Bruce has worked as senior designer with CPO Science since 2000 and collaborated with various teams to create all CPO book covers.

EQUIPMENT DESIGN

Thomas Narro – Senior Vice President
B.S., Mechanical Engineering, Rensselaer Polytechnic Institute
Accomplished design and manufacturing engineer; experienced consultant in corporate reengineering and industrial-environmental acoustics.

Danielle Dzurik
B.S., Industrial Design, Auburn University
Focuses her efforts in product development on creating new products and improving upon older designs.

MATERIAL SUPPORT

Kathryn Gavin – Purchasing and Quality Control Manager
Responsible for all functions related to purchasing raw materials and quality control of finished goods. Works closely with product development and design.

PROJECT AND TECHNICAL SUPPORT

Susan Gioia – Educational CPO Science Administrator
Expertise in office management. Oversees all functions necessary for the smooth product development of CPO products, including print and media.

Lynn L'Heureux
Owner of M&M Composition, LLC. Has worked in textbook composition for 10 years and specializes in math, computer, and science texts.

REVIEWERS

Mark Baker
Diamond, OH

Dr. Nicholas Benfaremo
South Portland, ME

Nancy Baker Cazan
SAMM Center
Massillon, OH

Ann Cleary
Medina High School
Medina, OH

Jean A. Cyders
McKinley High School
Canton, OH

Deirde L. Davenport
William Miller
Central Medical Magnet High School
Beaumont, TX

Dr. Gregorio Garcia
Brownsville ISD Department of Curriculum and Instruction
Brownsville, Texas

Cort Gillen
Cypress, TX

Alan P. Gnospelius
Design & Technology Academy
Northeast Independent School District
San Antonio, Texas

Lisa Q, Gothard
East Canton High School
East Canton, OH

Liz Gregory
Atkins High School
Austin, TX

James Max Hollon
Indiana

William C. Huckeba
Academy High School
Irving, TX

Chrystal Brooke Johnson
MacArthur High School
Irving, TX

Daniel Klein
Fairless High School
Navarre, OH

Kathleen Kuhn
Lake High School
Uniontown, OH

Jay Kurima
Fort Worth ISD
Texas

Ed Laubacher
Lake High School
Uniontown, OH

Matt Leatherberry
Minerva High School
Minerva, OH

John C. Lineweaver
Science Consultant
Abilene, Texas

Anita K. Marshall
Cypress, TX

Maria Estela Martinez
Irving Union Bower High School
Irving, TX

Chandra R. Maxey
Irving Union Bower High School
Irving, TX

Alyson Mazza
Salem High School
Salem, NH

Thomas McArthur
Hoover High School
North Canton, OH

Michael Mihalik
Lake High School
Uniontown, OH

William Miller
Arlington Heights High School
Ft Worth, TX

Kathryn Schommer Neuenschwander
Northrop High School
Indiana

Stacey L. Nunley
Mumford High School
Detroit, Michigan

Joel C. Palmer Ed. D.
Science Coordinator
Mesquite Independent School District
Texas

Neil Parrot
Tuslaw High School
Massillon, OH

Jeff Pickle
Hoover High School
North Canton, OH

Emily O. Price
Waxahachie High School
Texas

Julie Randolph
Odom Academy
Beaumont, TX

Steve Remenaric
Tuslaw High School
Massillon, OH

Jay Don Steele
Floresville High School
Floresville, TX

Ginger Torregrossa
Montgomery High School
Montgomery, TX

Timothy Totten
Fairless High School
Navarre, OH

Melissa Vela
Freelance Science Specialist
Brookline, NH

Michael Vela
Concord-Carlisle High School
Concord, MA

Elizabeth Volt
Science Curriculum Coordinator
Cleveland Metropolitan School District
Ohio

David Warner
Tuslaw High School
Massillon, OH

Dan Williamson
Irving High School
Irving, TX

Kathleen Mills
Rosharon, TX

Jaclyn L. Ziders
Lake High School
Uniontown, OH

How to Read an Investigation

Investigation title

Investigation number

Key question for the investigation

Steps
Proceed in order

Investigation procedures, equipment setup, and data collection

Questions you will answer

Materials list

Photo or illustration that helps in understanding the investigation

Data table

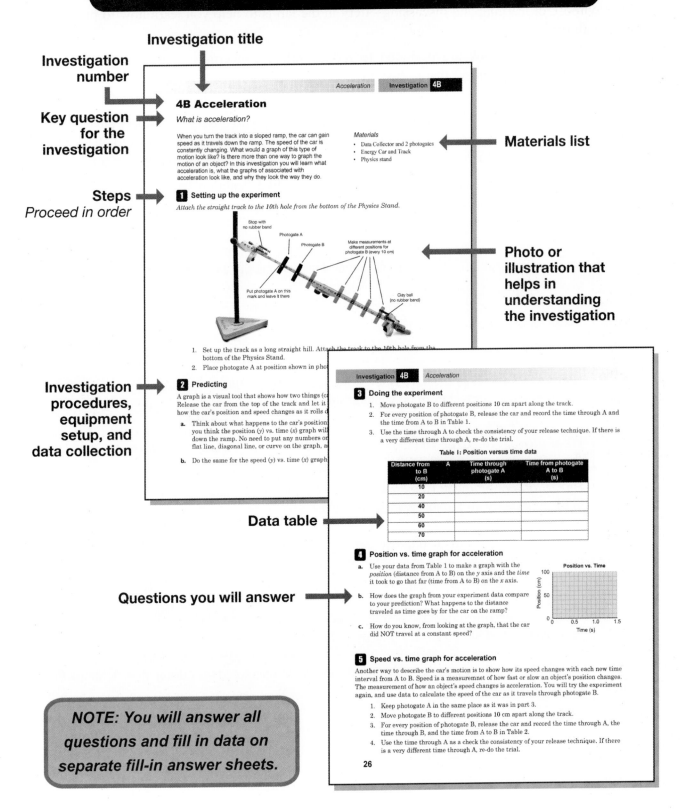

Acceleration Investigation **4B**

4B Acceleration

What is acceleration?

When you turn the track into a sloped ramp, the car can gain speed as it travels down the ramp. The speed of the car is constantly changing. What would a graph of this type of motion look like? Is there more than one way to graph the motion of an object? In this investigation you will learn what acceleration is, what the graphs of associated with acceleration look like, and why they look the way they do.

Materials
- Data Collector and 2 photogates
- Energy Car and Track
- Physics stand

1 Setting up the experiment

Attach the straight track to the 10th hole from the bottom of the Physics Stand.

Stop with no rubber band
Photogate A
Photogate B
Make measurements at different positions for photogate B (every 10 cm)
Put photogate A on this mark and leave it there
Clay ball (no rubber band)

1. Set up the track as a long straight hill. Attach the track to the 10th hole from the bottom of the Physics Stand.
2. Place photogate A at position shown in pho...

2 Predicting

A graph is a visual tool that shows how two things (c... Release the car from the top of the track and let it... how the car's position and speed changes as it rolls d...

a. Think about what happens to the car's position... you think the position (y) vs. time (x) graph will... down the ramp. No need to put any numbers o... flat line, diagonal line, or curve on the graph, a...

b. Do the same for the speed (y) vs. time (x) graph...

Investigation **4B** *Acceleration*

3 Doing the experiment

1. Move photogate B to different positions 10 cm apart along the track.
2. For every position of photogate B, release the car and record the time through A and the time from A to B in Table 1.
3. Use the time through A to check the consistency of your release technique. If there is a very different time through A, re-do the trial.

Table 1: Position versus time data

Distance from to B (cm)	A	Time through photogate A (s)	Time from photogate A to B (s)
10			
20			
40			
50			
60			
70			

4 Position vs. time graph for acceleration

a. Use your data from Table 1 to make a graph with the *position* (distance from A to B) on the *y* axis and the *time* it took to go that far (time from A to B) on the *x* axis.

b. How does the graph from your experiment data compare to your prediction? What happens to the distance traveled as time goes by for the car on the ramp?

c. How do you know, from looking at the graph, that the car did NOT travel at a constant speed?

Position vs. Time

5 Speed vs. time graph for acceleration

Another way to describe the car's motion is to show how its speed changes with each new time interval from A to B. Speed is a measuremnet of how fast or slow an object's position changes. The measurement of how an object's speed changes is acceleration. You will try the experiment again, and use data to calculate the speed of the car as it travels through photogate B.

1. Keep photogate A in the same place as it was in part 3.
2. Move photogate B to different positions 10 cm apart along the track.
3. For every position of photogate B, release the car and record the time through A, the time through B, and the time from A to B in Table 2.
4. Use the time through A as a check the consistency of your release technique. If there is a very different time through A, re-do the trial.

26

NOTE: You will answer all questions and fill in data on separate fill-in answer sheets.

LAB SAFETY

Observing safety precautions is an extremely important practice while completing science investigations. Using science equipment and carrying out laboratory procedures always require attention to safety. The purpose of learning and discussing safety in the lab is to help you learn how to protect yourself and others at all times.

The investigations in this book are designed to reduce safety concerns in the laboratory. The physics investigations use stable equipment that is easy to operate. The chemistry investigations use both household and laboratory chemicals. Although these chemicals might be familiar to you, they still must be used safely.

You will be introduced to safety by completing a skill sheet to help you observe the safety aids and important information in your science laboratory. In addition to this skill sheet, you may be asked to check your safety understanding and complete a safety contract. Your teacher will decide what is appropriate for your class.

Throughout this book, safety icons and words and phrases like "caution" and "safety tip" are used to highlight important safety information. Read the description for each icon carefully and look out for them when reading your book and doing investigations.

Safety	***General safety:*** Follow all instructions and safety rules to avoid injury to yourself or others.
	Wear safety goggles: Requires you to wear protective eyewear such as chemical splash goggles or safety glasses to prevent eye injuries.
	Wear a lab apron or coat: Requires you to wear a lab apron or coat to prevent damage to clothing and to protect from possible spills.
	Wear gloves: Requires you to protect your hands from injury due to heat or chemicals.
	Hazardous chemicals: Requires you to use extreme caution when working with chemicals in the laboratory and to follow all safety and disposal instructions from your teacher.
	Skin irritant: Requires you to use extreme caution when handling chemicals in the laboratory due to possible skin irritation and to follow all safety and disposal instructions from your teacher.
	Respiratory irritant: Requires you to perform the experiment under a laboratory hood and to avoid inhaling fumes while handling the chemicals.
	Laser: Requires you to use extreme caution while using a laser during investigations and to follow all safety instructions.
	Sharps: Requires you to use extreme caution when handling sharp objects such as scalpels or glass.
	Electrical: Use caution when working with electricity.

Lab safety is the responsibility of everyone! Help create a safe environment in your science lab by following the safety guidelines from your teacher as well as the guidelines discussed in this document.

Table of Contents

Optional Investigations

Lab Skills and Engineering Design Log

1A Measurement

Are you able to use scientific tools to make accurate measurements?

In everyday life, we use tools to make our work easier. For example, it is difficult to pound a nail without a hammer, to wrap a gift without tape, or to open plastic packages without scissors. In science, it is important to be able to correctly choose and use tools to make measurements. During the Measurement Games, you and a partner will practice choosing the correct tool to make accurate measurements.

Materials

- Paper cup
- Pebbles
- Water
- Masking tape
- 100-mL Graduated cylinder
- Electronic scale, or triple-beam balance
- Meter stick
- CPO DataCollector

1 Analyzing and interpreting data

a. Are you familiar with the tools used to make measurements of length, mass, and volume? From the list of materials above, choose the tool used to measure each property.

Property	Tool used
Length	
Mass	
Volume	

b. Do you know what metric units describe length, mass, and volume measurements? Discuss this with your partner, and write an appropriate unit that corresponds to each property.

Property	Unit used
Length	
Mass	
Volume	

c. Read about the events listed in Part 2 below, and predict your outcome in each event before you actually perform the task.

Event	Prediction
Straw Javelin	
Paper Cup	
Pebble Grab	
Side Step	
Hoppity Hop	

1

2 Doing the activity

A. Perform the event, and collect and record data

1. **Straw Javelin:** During this event, you will throw a straw as far as you can. Your front foot may not cross the start line, and you must throw the straw like a javelin using only one hand. Measure the distance of your throw in meters and centimeters.

2. **Paper Cup Challenge:** How much water can you move from a tank to a beaker in 10 seconds using just one paper cup? Use a graduated cylinder to measure the volume of water you successfully transfer. Be careful not to spill any water!

3. **Pebble Grab:** Who can grab the greatest mass of pebbles? Use only one hand to grab as many pebbles as you can out of a container. Transfer them to an electronic balance to measure the mass. Be sure the balance is measuring in the correct units before you begin.

4. **Side Step:** How far is your leg span? From a starting point, step as far as you can to the side. Your partner will measure the length of your side step in meters and centimeters.

5. **Hoppity Hop:** Who can hop (on one foot) 10 meters the fastest? Mark 10 meters on the floor with the masking tape. Use the data collector in stopwatch mode to time the race. Lightly tap the screen to start and stop the timer. Tap "reset" in between trials or races. Time how long it takes your partner to hop 10 meters on one foot!

B. Game results

1. Record your results in the data table below. Any result with missing or incorrect units will be automatically disqualified.

2. After you have recorded your results, find out who the winners are in each event. Decide who has the best score in your group for each event. Use that score for the class data set. Record the data in the data table your teacher has drawn on the board. Determine the best overall score for each event, and record the winning results in the data table below.

Event	My results	Winning results
Straw Javelin		
Paper Cup Challenge		
Pebble Grab		
Side Step		
Hoppity Hop		

3 Constructing explanations

a. Calculate the difference between the winning result and your result for each event. (Don't forget units!)

Event	Difference
Straw Javelin	
Paper Cup Challenge	
Pebble Grab	
Side Step	
Hoppity Hop	

b. In which event were you closest to the winner?

c. In which event were you the farthest from the winner?

d. How close were your results to your predictions?

e. Which measurement were you most familiar with before the games? Why?

f. Which measurement did you find easiest to make during the games? Why do you think it was so easy?

g. Which measurement did you find hardest to make? Why was it hard?

4 Exploring on your own

a. Scientists work hard to be precise in their measurements. When measuring in real life, most of us are accurate enough but hardly precise. Do you know the difference? Look it up and draw several examples that represent the difference between *accuracy* and *precision*.

b. Create a quiz that your classmates could take that would test their knowledge of the different measuring tools used in a science lab and their appropriate units. Include an answer key.

c. Find a science article from a magazine, newspaper, or website that describes scientists measuring something. Explain in a one-paragraph summary what they are measuring, what tools they are using or could use to make the measurements, and the units associated with the measurements.

1B Conversion Chains

How can you use unit canceling to solve conversion problems?

$$115 \text{ km} \times \frac{1 \text{ mi}}{1.6 \text{ km}} = 72 \text{ mi}$$

Suppose you are traveling in Canada or Mexico and you see a sign that says the next city is 115 kilometers away. How many miles is that? You could use the dimensional analysis process to figure it out. Dimensional analysis is a method of using conversion factors and unit canceling to solve unit conversion problems. In this activity, you will use conversion chains to start and solve conversions.

Materials

- CPO Conversion Chain card deck
- Conversion chain table for recording chains and solutions
- Calculator

1 Conversion Chain cards

The deck of cards contains

12 START cards, 12 SOLVE cards, 36 conversion factor cards

1. Look at the cards to identify what START, SOLVE, and conversion factor cards look like.
2. Shuffle the cards thoroughly.

2 Creating conversion chains

The object of the game is to have the most points after solving six conversion chains.

1. Deal four cards to each player (works best with three to five players). Assign a scorekeeper.
2. Choose a player to go first. This player must play a START card from his or her hand or draw a card from the deck. If the player draws a START card, it may be played; otherwise play passes to the next player. Play passes until a START card has been played. Anytime a START card is played, the player scores 5 points.
3. The next player may play another START card or a conversion card that will continue the conversion chain. That means that the card must have a denominator unit that matches a START card unit, to cancel the starting unit and continue the chain. Only six START cards can be played in a game.

4. Even if the player has more than one conversion card that could be played on multiple START cards, the player must choose only one card to play on each turn.

5. After playing a card, the player must draw a card.

6. If the player does not have a suitable card, the player must draw one card from the deck. If the card will play, the player can play it. If the card won't play, the player must pass this turn.

7. The next player plays a conversion factor card, plays a START card, or draws a card, and play continues.

8. A team can have as many as three conversion chains going at once.

9. After a minimum of three conversion factor cards have been played on any particular START card, any player is allowed to play a SOLVE card on his or her turn, and the player *immediately scores 5 points for each conversion chain card in the chain.*

3 Solving a chain and scoring points

1. Anytime a SOLVE card is played on any conversion chain, all players must record the chain on the answer sheet and calculate the answer with the correct number of significant digits and unit.

2. Players compare answers and determine who has the correct answer. Consult your teacher if there are disagreements.

3. *Any* player with the correct answer scores 25 points.

4. Keep playing until your team has created and solved six conversion chains.

5. At the end of the game, after six conversion chains have been scored, players must subtract 5 points per card for unplayed cards remaining in the hand.

6. Total up the points, subtract the unused cards, and determine the winner.

4 Reminders and strategies

1. Whenever you play a START card, you score 5 points. If you draw a START card after six chains have already been started, you must keep that card in your hand, and it will cost you 5 points in the end.

2. Remember, you always draw a card at the end of every turn.

3. When a conversion chain has been solved, place the START, chain, and SOLVE cards to the side in a pile. You might want to look at a solved chain later in the game. Also, this will help your team keep track of how many conversion chains have been solved (the goal is to solve six).

4. You can play a SOLVE card only after there are at least three conversion factor cards in any chain. For beginners, a SOLVE card should be played after three chain cards are in a chain. For advanced players, a SOLVE card can be held back and played after the chain is much longer. The SOLVE card player benefits, since that player earns 5 points for each chain card in the chain.

5. Record each conversion chain your team creates in Table 1. There are blanks for recording six conversion factors per chain. If a chain has fewer than six, just leave remaining boxes blank. If you need more than six, continue on the back of the page.

6. The first row of Table 1 shows an example chain.

Table 1: Conversion Chains

START card							Answer with correct sig digs and unit	Points scored
46.3 m	$x\dfrac{1\ km}{1000\ m}$	$x\dfrac{1\ mi}{1.6\ km}$	$x\dfrac{5280\ ft}{1\ mi}$	$\times\ \underline{\quad}$	$\times\ \underline{\quad}$	$\times\ \underline{\quad}$	153 ft	
	$\times\ \underline{\quad}$	$\times\ \underline{\quad}$	$\times\ \underline{\quad}$	$\times\ \underline{\quad}$	$\times\ \underline{\quad}$	$\times\ \underline{\quad}$		
	$\times\ \underline{\quad}$	$\times\ \underline{\quad}$	$\times\ \underline{\quad}$	$\times\ \underline{\quad}$	$\times\ \underline{\quad}$	$\times\ \underline{\quad}$		
	$\times\ \underline{\quad}$	$\times\ \underline{\quad}$	$\times\ \underline{\quad}$	$\times\ \underline{\quad}$	$\times\ \underline{\quad}$	$\times\ \underline{\quad}$		
	$\times\ \underline{\quad}$	$\times\ \underline{\quad}$	$\times\ \underline{\quad}$	$\times\ \underline{\quad}$	$\times\ \underline{\quad}$	$\times\ \underline{\quad}$		
	$\times\ \underline{\quad}$	$\times\ \underline{\quad}$	$\times\ \underline{\quad}$	$\times\ \underline{\quad}$	$\times\ \underline{\quad}$	$\times\ \underline{\quad}$		
	$\times\ \underline{\quad}$	$\times\ \underline{\quad}$	$\times\ \underline{\quad}$	$\times\ \underline{\quad}$	$\times\ \underline{\quad}$	$\times\ \underline{\quad}$		
							TOTAL	

5 Thinking about the game

a. The conversion chains you create for this game could be quite long, and the actual conversions could be solved with fewer conversion factors. What is the least number of conversion factors you would need to make these conversions, given the cards in the deck?

- converting ft to cm

- converting mi to m

b. Because of the limitations of the cards in the deck, to convert km to cm you have to go through English units. What is a much easier way to convert kilometers to centimeters? Explain.

c. Explain the math reasoning for being able to "cancel" like units that appear in the numerator and denominator of conversion factors in a conversion chain.

2A Mass, Volume, and Indirect Measurement

How can you find the mass of a single grain of rice?

In this investigation, you will find the average mass of a single grain of rice. One grain of rice is too small to register a mass value on your electronic scale. Scientists often need to measure something that is too small or too large to measure directly. In such situations, scientists often use methods of indirect measurement. In indirect measurement, you calculate a measurement you *can't* make from other measurements that you *can* make.

Materials (per group)

- About 1/4 cup of rice
- Cellophane tape
- Electronic scale (or triple-beam balance)
- Scissors
- Index card

1 Getting started

To find the average mass of a single grain of rice, you will first measure the mass of a 1-cubic centimeter box filled with rice. Next, you will count how many grains are in the cube. Then, by dividing the mass of the cube by the number of grains in the cube, you will get a good indirect measurement of the average mass of a single grain of rice.

The first thing you need to do is find out how many grains of rice are in a cubic centimeter.

Fold and tape a 1-cm box.

Count how many grains of rice fill the box.

1. Cut out and fold up the small cube (made out of an index card) as shown in the diagram. Use tape to hold the cube together. This cube has a volume of 1 cubic centimeter (1 cm^3 or 1 cc).
2. Fill the cube level with rice.
3. Carefully empty the rice in the cube onto the table. Count how many grains fit into the cube, and record the value in Table 1.

4. Calculate the number of grains of rice per cubic centimeter, and record this value in Table 1. Use this formula: *number of grains / volume of cube = grains per cubic centimeter.*

Table 1: Data on number of rice grains per cubic centimeter

Volume of cube (cm³)	1
Number of grains of rice	
Calculated grains per cubic centimeter	

2 Accuracy, precision, and resolution

No instrument in science makes perfect measurements. A single cubic centimeter of rice is a very small mass and difficult to measure precisely with an ordinary scale. For example, suppose you want a measurement that is precise to 1 percent. A typical electronic scale has a resolution of 0.1 grams. That means the smallest mass you can measure with this scale is 100 times as large as its resolution (100×0.1 g = 10 g). Therefore, 10 grams is the smallest mass you can measure to a precision of 1 percent. Since the mass of one cubic centimeter of rice is less than 10 grams, we will use a much larger amount of rice.

3 Making a precise measurement

1. Cut out and fold up the 3-centimeter cube as shown in the diagram. Use tape to hold the cube together.

Make and fill a 3-cm box with rice.

2. Calculate the cube's volume (length × width × depth), and record in Table 2.

3. Place the cube on the scale, and reset the scale to zero. The scale display should now read 0.0 grams.

4. Remove the cardboard cube, and fill it level with rice. Place the filled cube back on the scale, and record the mass.

5. Calculate the number of grains of rice in the cube based on the value of grains per cubic centimeter you calculated in Table 1.

6. Use the mass of rice in the large cube and the calculated number of rice grains to find the average mass of one grain of rice.

Table 2: Data on the mass of a grain of rice

Volume of cube (cm³)		**Number of grains of rice in 3-cm cube**	
Mass of rice in cube (g)		**Calculated mass of 1 grain of rice (g)**	

4 Analyzing and interpreting data

a. Why did the scale show a small negative mass when you removed the empty cardboard cube at the beginning of Part 3, step 4?

b. Why does this investigation measure the *average* mass instead of the *actual* mass of a grain of rice?

c. Why is the average mass a more useful quantity than the actual mass of any single grain of rice?

d. Compare your average mass of one grain of rice with other groups' results. How do your results compare? Discuss your findings in a few sentences.

2B Density

How is an object's density related to its volume, mass, and tendency to sink or float?

You may be familiar with the trick question, "Which is heavier: a pound of feathers or a pound of bricks?" The answer, of course, is that they have the same weight. However, the pound of feathers has a much greater volume because feathers have a much lower density than bricks. The brick material is squeezed together tightly, while the feathers contain a large amount of empty space. In this investigation, you will study the relationship between mass, volume, and density. You will also determine how an object's density affects whether it sinks or floats in water.

Materials

- Balance
- Displacement tank
- Disposable cup
- 250-mL Beaker
- Set of six identical objects
- 100-mL Graduated cylinder
- Graph paper
- Density cubes
- Metric ruler
- Water
- Paper towels

1 Measuring mass and volume

1. Each lab group has a unique set of six identical objects. Using a balance and a displacement tank, find the mass and volume of one of your objects. Add a second object, and find the total mass and volume of both objects. Then find the total mass and volume of three, four, and five objects. Record your data in Table 1. Note: Although your objects look identical, there may be small differences. Do not obtain your data by multiplying the mass or volume of one object by the number of objects you have. Use the displacement method for measuring density.

Table 1: Mass and volume data

	One object	Two objects	Three objects	Four objects	Five objects
Mass (g)					
Volume (mL)					

2. Plot your data on graph paper. Label the *x*-axis "volume" and the *y*-axis "mass." Be sure to use the entire space on your graph paper for making your graph.

2 Analyzing your data

a. Is there any pattern to the data points on your graph? For example, the points might form a smooth curve, a straight line, a random scattering, or a cluster in a certain region. Describe any pattern you see.

b. Line up your ruler along the points on your graph so it is as close as possible to all of the dots. The line may not touch all of the dots but should have an equal number of dots on each side. This line is called the "line of best fit." Draw the line.

c. Find the slope of the line of best fit. To do this, choose any two points on the line. These will be represented as (X_1, Y_1) and (X_2, Y_2). Use the formula below to calculate the slope of the line.

$$\frac{(Y_2 - Y_1)}{(X_2 - X_1)} = \text{slope}$$

The slope tells how many grams of matter are contained in each milliliter of material. Some substances, like lead, have many grams of matter packed into each milliliter. Other substances, like styrofoam, have less than a single gram of matter packed into each milliliter.

d. Compare your slope with the results obtained by other groups. Are your slopes similar or different? If different, explain what may have caused any differences.

e. The relationship between a substance's mass and volume is called its density. What is the density of the material you tested?

3 Using your model

a. Your graph shows data for five objects. Use your graph to predict the mass of *six* objects.

b. Next, use the balance to find the total mass of all six objects.

c. How does your predicted value from your graph compare to the measured mass obtained using the balance?

d. Use the mass that you found in step b. Find that number on the *y*-axis of your graph. Then, find the point on the line with that *y*-value. What is the *x*-value of the point?

e. Now, find the volume of all six objects experimentally.

f. How does the *x*-value from the graph compare with the measured volume?

4 Comparing class data

Collect data from each group in the class to fill in Table 2.

Table 2: Class data for density of objects

	Group1	Group 2	Group 3	Group 4	Group 5	Group 6
Volume of one object (mL)						
Type of material						
Density (g/mL)						

Using the data from Table 2, answer the following questions.

a. Does density depend on the size of the material? Give evidence to support your answer.

b. Does density depend on the type of material? Give evidence to support your answer.

c. Using what you have observed in this lab, do you suppose that density depends on the shape of the material? Why or why not?

5 Using a different method to find volume

You used the displacement method to find the volume of your objects in Part 1 of the investigation. The displacement method works because an object's volume is equal to the volume of water it displaces, or pushes aside. This method is useful for objects with complicated, or irregular, shapes.

If an object has a simple shape, such as a cube, its volume can be found by measuring its dimensions. The volume of a cube is found using this formula:

Volume = length × width × height

When length, width, and height are measured in centimeters, volume is in cubic centimeters or cm^3. A 1 cm × 1 cm × 1 cm cube displaces 1 milliliter of water, so 1 cm^3 = 1 milliliter.

1. Use the method demonstrated in the diagram on the right to measure the length, width, and height of the steel cube in centimeters.

2. Record your measurements in Table 3.

3. Calculate the volume of the steel cube. Record your volume calculation in cubic centimeters in Table 3.

4. Repeat steps 1–3 for the other four cubes. Record the volumes in Table 3.

Table 3: Cube volume table

Material of solid cube	Length (cm)	Width (cm)	Height (cm)	Volume from calculation (cm^3)
Steel				
Oak				
Aluminum				
Copper				
PVC				

6 Calculating the density

The cubes' volumes are almost exactly the same, but their masses are different because they are all made of different materials. Use Table 4 to calculate the density of each cube. First, record the volume of each cube from Table 3 data.

1. Use a balance to determine the mass of the steel cube, and record it in Table 4.
2. Divide the mass of the steel cube by the volume to calculate its density: density (g/cm^3) = mass (g) / volume (cm^3). Record the density value in Table 4.
3. Repeat steps 1 and 2 to find the density of each cube.

Table 4: Cube density data

Material of solid cube	Mass (g)	Volume (cm^3)	Density (g/cm^3)	Prediction (sink or float)	Result (sink or float)
Steel					
Oak					
Aluminum					
Copper					
PVC					

7 Analyzing and interpreting data

a. How do the five volumes compare? Why might they be different?

b. Pick up and hold each cube. Predict whether it will sink or float in water. Record your predictions in Table 4. What did you base your predictions on?

c. What is the density of water in g/cm^3?

d. Compare the density of water to the density you calculated for each cube. Take another look at your sink/float predictions. Make any changes you need to, based on your density comparisons.

e. What rule did you use to make your prediction? Summarize the rule in one sentence.

8 Testing the hypothesis

Your predictions from step 7d, and the rule from step 7e, represent a hypothesis. Test the hypothesis by dropping each cube in a beaker of water. Record your results in Table 4.

9 Constructing explanations

a. Describe two ways to find the density of a regular-shaped object like a cube.

b. Explain why two objects can have equal volumes but different masses.

c. Which method of prediction was better, testing the weight of the cube in your hand or comparing the density of the cube to the density of water? Why?

3A Measuring Time

How is time measured accurately?

A measurement is a quantity with a unit that tells what the quantity means. For example, 3 seconds is a measurement of time that includes a quantity (3) and a unit (seconds). This investigation will explore time measurement.

Materials

- CPO DataCollector and 2 photogates

1 Using the DataCollector as a stopwatch

A stopwatch measures a *time interval*. The DataCollector stopwatch shows time in seconds up to 60 seconds. The display shows *min:sec:hundredths* for times longer than 1 minute.

1. Select the DataCollector's stopwatch mode from the home screen.
2. Practice starting and stopping the stopwatch.
3. Reset the stopwatch to zero.

2 Observing reaction time

The time it takes a signal from your brain to move a muscle is called *reaction time*.

1. This experiment takes two people. One person (the watcher) watches the stopwatch, and the other person (the operator) pushes the buttons without looking at the display. The watcher selects a time between 5 and 10 seconds and keeps the time secret.
2. The operator starts (and stops) the stopwatch *without looking at the display*. The watcher looks at the display and says STOP at the secret time. For example, if the secret time is 6 seconds, the watcher should say STOP when the display reaches 6.00 seconds.
3. Repeat the experiment several times, record your results in Table 1, and calculate reaction time by taking an average of the difference between secret time and measured time for all five trials.

Table I: Reaction time

Trial	Secret time (s)	Measured time (s)	Difference (s)	Avg. difference or reaction time (s)
1				
2				
3				
4				
5				

3 Mixed units for time

In physical science, you are usually going to measure time in seconds. However, time is often given in mixed units, which may include hours, minutes, and seconds. Consider the following three time intervals.

1. 16,000 seconds
2. 250 minutes
3. 4 hours, 23 minutes, and 15 seconds (4:23:15)

a. Which time interval is in mixed units?

b. Which time is longest? Shortest?

c. You know that 1 minute = 60 seconds; how many seconds is 250 minutes?

d. You know that 1 hour = 60 minutes; how many minutes are in 4 hours?

e. Use your answer from question d to figure out how many seconds are in 4:23:15.

f. Arrange the three measurements from shortest to longest.

4 Using the photogates

A photogate allows us to use an infrared light beam to start and stop the DataCollector. When the CPO timer mode is on the interval function, it uses photogates to control the clock.

1. Connect a single photogate to the Photogate A input with a cord.
2. Select *interval function* in the CPO timer mode of the DataCollector.
3. Try blocking the infrared beam with your finger, and observe what happens on the timer display.

Try your own experiments until you can answer the following questions. Be very specific in your answers. Someone who has never used the DataCollector before should be able to read your answers and know what to do with the infrared beam to make the clock start and stop.

a. How do you start the clock?

b. How do you stop the clock?

c. What time interval has the clock measured?

5 Using two photogates

1. Connect a second photogate to the DataCollector.
2. Make sure the light on each photogate is green, and press the reset button. Pressing reset clears the clocks and also tells the DataCollector to look at its inputs to see which photogates are connected.
3. Do your own experiments, and fill in the rest of Table 2.

Table 2: Timer and photogate rules

t_A	
How do you start the t_A clock?	
How do you stop the t_A clock?	

t_B	
How do you start the t_B clock?	
How do you stop the t_B clock?	

t_{AB}	
How do you start the t_{AB} clock?	
How do you stop the t_{AB} clock?	

3B Experiments and Variables

How do you design a valid experiment?

Experiments help us collect evidence so we can unlock nature's puzzles. If an experiment is well planned, the results can provide an answer to a scientific question like "What would happen if I did this?" If the experiment is not well planned, you will still get results, but you may not know what they mean. In this investigation, you will experiment with a car on a ramp. Only by paying careful attention to the variables can you make sense of the results.

Materials

- CPO Energy Car and Track
- CPO DataCollector and 2 photogates
- CPO Physics Stand

1 Setting up the experiment

1. Set up the track as a long, straight section. Your teacher will tell you which hole in the stand to use to attach the track. Each group will use a different hole and have a different ramp angle.
2. Put a clay ball on the stop at the bottom.
3. Place two photogates on the track with photogate A higher than photogate B.
4. Release the car and record the time it takes the car to pass between the photogates (t_{AB}).

2 Making a prediction

a. Which track should have the fastest car? Which track should have the shortest time between photogates?

b. Write a one-sentence hypothesis that relates the time between photogates to the angle of the track.

c. Use Table 1 to record the results from each group in your class. Record the times in the column labeled First trial. Leave the column labeled Second trial blank. How do the results compare with your hypothesis? Can you give a reason why the cars did or did not behave as you expected?

Table I: Photogate times from A to B

Attachment hole (holes from bottom)	First trial Time from A to B (s)	Second trial Time from A to B (s)

3 Variables

a. List at least six variables in your system that affect the time between photogates.

b. Which variable is the experimental variable? How do you know?

c. What should be done with the other variables (other than the experimental variable)? Why?

d. Name two variables that should *not* be included in your system. (These variables are ones that do not have much or any influence on the time from photogate A to B.)

4 A controlled experiment

1. With your teacher and the rest of your class, decide how to control the variables other than the experimental variable.
2. Practice rolling the car until you can get three consecutive times within 0.0010 seconds of each other.
3. Repeat the experiment using the experimental and controlled variables you discussed and decided on. Record the new data in the column labeled Second trial.

5 Arguing from evidence

a. Does the second trial of the experiment produce results that support your hypothesis?

b. Why do you think this is so?

c. If the results you expect do not occur, discuss what you could do to find the problem. List at least three steps that relate to variables, experiments, and controls.

4A Speed

Can you predict the speed of the car as it moves down the track?

What happens to the speed of a car as it rolls down a ramp? Does the speed stay constant or does it change? In this investigation, you will measure the speed of a car at different points as it rolls down a ramp. Then, you will make a graph that describes the motion and predict the speed of the car somewhere on the ramp.

Materials

• CPO DataCollector and 1 photogate
• CPO Energy Car and Track
• CPO Physics Stand

1 Describing speed

Suppose you ran in a race. What information would you need in order to describe your speed? Saying that you ran for 20 minutes would not be enough information. To describe your speed, you would need two things:

1. The *distance* you traveled, and

2. The *time* it took you to travel that distance.

Example	Distance	Time	Speed
10 seconds / 100 meters	100 meters	10 seconds	10 m/s
1 hour / 50 miles	50 miles	1 hour	50 mph
15 seconds / 10 feet	10 feet	15 seconds	0.67 ft/s

Based on the examples above, fill in the boxes to complete the equation for calculating speed.

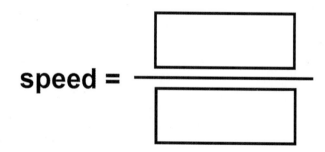

$$\text{speed} = \frac{\boxed{}}{\boxed{}}$$

2 Making a hypothesis

Where on the ramp is the car going fastest? Is it going fastest at the top, the middle, or the bottom?

a. Create a hypothesis about the car's speed on the ramp. State where it is moving fastest and why you think so.

3 Setting up the investigation

Flag on car is just about to break beam on photogate.

Photogate

Clay ball at end of adjustment screw

1. Join the two ends of the ramp labeled Energy Car to each other. The ramp should be straight, without a bend in the middle. Use two threaded knobs to connect the two parts.
2. Attach the ramp to the Physics Stand using one threaded knob. Your teacher will tell your group which hole on the stand to use. Hole where the ramp is attached: _____
3. Place a bumper at each end of the ramp. Place a clay ball on the end of the thumb screw at the bottom of the ramp to stop the car. The thumb screw at the top of the ramp will be the place where you start the car.
4. Attach a photogate to the Photogate A input of the DataCollector.
5. Place the photogate so its screw is on the round mark that is closest to the front of the car.

4 Using the photogate to measure speed

As the car passes through the photogate, the DataCollector clock starts and stops. The DataCollector measures the length of time that the light beam is broken. Speed is equal to the distance traveled divided by the time taken. What distance do you use?

Notice the small "flag" on one side of the car. This is the part of the car that blocks the photogate's light beam. The distance the car moves while the light is blocked is the width of the flag, 1 centimeter.

Distance   **Time**

1 cm ⊢⊣ ⸻ flag

`0.125`

Start timing.   Finish timing.

a. What is the *distance* traveled by the car in the example?

b. What is the *time* taken by the car in the example?

c. What is the *speed* of the car in the example?

5 Doing the investigation

Distance

Position of photogate
Measure the distance from the front of the flag to the center of the photogate.

1. Place the car at the top of the ramp. Place the photogate 10 centimeters downhill from the car. Measure the distance from the front edge of the car's flag to the middle of the screw that holds the photogate to the track. Measuring is easier if you line up the car's flag over one of the circular marks because the marks are 5 centimeters apart. Record the photogate's position in Table 1.

2. Release the car without pushing it. Record the time through photogate A in Table 1.

3. Calculate the speed of the car using the distance traveled (1 cm) and the time at photogate A.

4. Move the photogate 10 centimeters farther down the track, and repeat the trial. Record the position, time, and speed.

5. Repeat the measurements of position, time, and speed for six different places spaced along the ramp. You will have to skip some places in the middle of the track where the photogate won't attach.

Table 1: Position, time, and speed data

Position of photogate A (cm)	Time through photogate A (s)	Distance traveled by the car (cm)	Speed of the car (cm/s)
		1.00	
		1.00	
		1.00	
		1.00	
		1.00	
		1.00	

6 Arguing from evidence

a. From your measurements, what can you say about the car's speed as it moves down the ramp?

b. Use your data to make a graph that shows how the car's speed changes as it rolls down the ramp. Put speed on the *y*-axis and position of the photogate on the *x*-axis. Be certain to label the axes with the correct variable and the proper unit of measurement. Give the graph a descriptive title. Include the number of the hole you used to connect the ramp to the stand in your title.

c. Describe what the graph shows about how the speed of the car is changing as it moves down the ramp.

d. Compare your graph with that of students who connected their ramps at different heights on the stand. Explain any differences you see.

7 Using your graph

Now that you have gathered, organized, and analyzed your data, it is time to use it to make a prediction. You measured the speed of the car at several places on the ramp as it rolled to the bottom. Now you will predict what the speed of the car will be at a place where you did not measure. You can do this using the information represented by your graph.

1. In Table 2 record a position on the ramp where you did not measure the speed of the car. The position should be between two places where you *did* measure the speed.

Table 2: Predicted speed data

Selected position (cm)	Predicted speed at selected position (cm/s)	Actual speed at selected position (cm/s)	Percent correct of prediction

2. Use your graph to find the predicted speed of the car at the selected position. To do this, start on the *x*-axis at the position you have selected. Draw a line straight up until it interesects with the speed vs. position line on your graph. At the intersection point, draw a line horizontally over to the *y*-axis where the speed is recorded. This is the speed that corresponds to your new location. The graph to the right uses a position of 55 centimeters as an example. Use a different position. Record your predicted speed in Table 2.

3. Place the photogate at the position you selected in step 1, and record the time it takes for the car to pass through the photogate.

4. Use the flag width (1.00 centimeter) and the time to calculate the speed. Record the actual speed in Table 2.

8 Calculating percent error

a. Find the difference between the predicted speed and the actual speed.

Predicted speed – Actual speed = Difference

b. Take this difference, divide it by the predicted speed, and then multiply by 100.

(Difference ÷ Predicted speed) × 100 = Percent error

c. Use the percent error to calculate percent correct. Record percent correct in Table 2.

100 – Percent error = Percent correct

d. What do you think can account for any error you may have had?

4B Acceleration

What is acceleration?

When you turn the track into a sloped ramp, the car can gain speed as it travels down the ramp. The speed of the car is constantly changing. What would a graph of this type of motion look like? Is there more than one way to graph the motion of an object? In this investigation, you will learn what acceleration is, what the graphs associated with acceleration look like, and why they look the way they do.

Materials

- CPO DataCollector and 2 photogates
- CPO Energy Car and Track
- CPO Physics Stand

1 Setting up the investigation

1. Set up the track as a long, straight ramp. Attach the track to the tenth hole from the bottom of the Physics Stand.
2. Place photogate A at the position shown in the photo. Keep photogate A in this position.

2 Developing a model

A graph is a visual tool that shows how two things (called variables) are related. Release the car from the top of the track, and let it roll down the track a few times. Observe how the car's position and speed change as it rolls down the track.

a. Think about what happens to the car's position as it rolls down the track. Sketch what you think the position (*y*) vs. time (*x*) graph will look like for the Energy Car as it moves down the ramp. No need to put any numbers on the axes, just label the axes and place a flat line, diagonal line, or curve on the graph, according to your prediction.

b. Do the same for the speed (*y*) vs. time (*x*) graph prediction.

3 Doing the investigation

1. Move photogate B to different positions along the ramp, each time 10 cm farther from photogate A.
2. For every position of photogate B, release the car and record the time through A and the time from A to B in Table 1.
3. Use the time through A to check the consistency of your release technique. If you notice a very different time through A, redo the trial.

Table 1: Position vs. time data

Distance from A to B (cm)	Time through photogate A (s)	Time from photogate A to B (s)
10		
20		
40		
50		
60		
70		

4 Position vs. time graph for acceleration

a. Use your data from Table 1 to make a graph with the *position* (distance from A to B) on the *y*-axis and the *time* it took to go that far (time from A to B) on the *x*-axis.

b. How does the graph from your experiment data compare to your prediction? What happens to the distance traveled as time goes by for the car on the ramp?

c. How do you know, from looking at the graph, that the car did *not* travel at a constant speed?

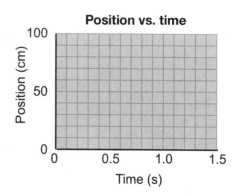

5 Speed vs. time graph for acceleration

Another way to describe the car's motion is to show how its speed changes with each new time interval from A to B. Speed is the measurement of how quickly or slowly an object's position changes. Acceleration is the measurement of how an object's speed changes. You will try the experiment again and this time, use data to calculate the speed of the car as it travels through photogate B.

1. Keep photogate A in the same position as it was in Part 3.
2. Move photogate B to different positions 10 centimeters apart along the track.
3. For every position of photogate B, release the car and record the time through A, the time through B, and the time from A to B in Table 2.
4. Use the time through A to check the consistency of your release technique. If you notice a very different time through A, redo the trial.

Table 2: Speed vs. time data

Distance from A to B (cm)	Time through photogate A (s)	Time through photogate B (s)	Time from photogate A to B (s)	Speed at photogate B (cm/s)
10				
20				
40				
50				
60				
70				

5. How fast is the car going as it travels through B each time? Calculate the speed (v) of the car at each position of photogate B. Record your speeds in Table 2.

$$v = \frac{d}{t} \qquad v = \frac{1.00 \text{ cm}}{\text{time B}}$$

a. Draw a graph with the *speed* (speed at B) on the *y*-axis and the *time* it took to go that far (time from A to B) on the *x*-axis.

b. How does the graph from your experiment data compare to your prediction?

c. What happens to the speed as time goes by for the car on the downhill ramp?

Speed v.s time

6 Arguing from evidence

a. Did the car accelerate, or change speed, as it traveled down the ramp? Justify your answer.

b. Use the formula for acceleration to find the average acceleration of your car. Use data from the trial in Table 2 where photogate B was 70 centimeters from A. The unit for acceleration will be cm/s/s.

$$acceleration = \frac{final\ velocity - initial\ velocity}{time\ elapsed} \qquad acceleration\ of\ car = \frac{speed\ B - speed\ A}{time\ A\ to\ B}$$

c. Use your speed vs. time graph to predict how much time it will take for the car to reach a speed of 200 cm/s.

d. Use your position vs. time graph to predict where on the track the car would reach a speed of 200 cm/s.

e. Test your predictions with a photogate at your predicted location on the track. Were your predictions accurate? Record your observations.

5A What Is a Newton?

What is force, and how is it measured?

You can think of force as a push or pull. Objects interact with each other (and you) through forces. It takes force to start an object's motion and stop an object in motion. This investigation will explore the precise definition of force and measure the strength of forces.

Materials

- Spring scale (0–5 N)
- 15 Round metal washers (1/2-inch inner diameter)
- Loop of string
- Electronic scale (or triple-beam balance)

1 Measuring forces

Forces have two important properties: strength and direction. In the English system of units, the strength of a force is measured in pounds. When you measure your own weight in pounds, you are measuring the force of gravity acting on your body. In the metric system, the strength of a force is measured in newtons (N). A quarter-pound hamburger has a weight of about 1 newton (1 lb = 4.448 N).

1. You can measure force with a spring scale. Before using a spring scale, however, you must be sure it correctly starts at zero. Calibrate the spring scale by turning the nut on the top until the plunger lines up with the zero mark.

2. Pull on the hook so the spring extends. When you pull, you are applying a force. Can you pull with a force of 2 newtons (2 N)?

Turn the plastic nut.

The top of the plunger should line up with zero.

2 Weight: The force of gravity

Weight is a common, familiar force. Objects that have mass also have weight. Weight is a measure of the action of gravity on an object's mass.

1. Attach three steel washers to a loop of string.

2. Use a calibrated spring scale to measure the weight of the washers in newtons (N).

3. Use an electronic scale or triple-beam balance to measure the washers' mass in grams (g). Convert mass in grams to kilograms (divide by 1,000 or move the decimal point three places to the left).

4. Repeat the experiment for 6, 9, 12, and 15 washers.

Table 1: Weight and mass data

Number of washers	Weight (N)	Mass (g)	Mass (kg)
3			
6			
9			
12			
15			

3 Analyzing and interpreting data

What do the results of your investigation tell you about the relationship between weight in newtons and mass in kilograms? Create a graph as described below to answer this question.

a. Make a graph of your data from Table 1. Place weight in newtons on the vertical (y) axis and mass in kilograms on the horizontal (x) axis.

b. Describe the graph. What does it tell you about the relationship between mass and weight?

c. Calculate the slope of your graph. The slope is equal to the strength of gravity (g) on Earth, measured in newtons per kilogram (N/kg).

d. Write an equation that relates weight in newtons, mass in kilograms, and the strength of gravity (g). It should be in the form: weight = _____

e. If an object has a mass of 10 kilograms, how much does it weigh in newtons?

4 Arguing from evidence

a. Explain how you could estimate the weight and mass of seven of your steel washers. What is your estimate?

b. Find the weight and mass for seven washers. How close is the actual value to your estimated value? Explain some reasons why your value may not be perfectly accurate.

5B Friction

How does friction affect motion?

Friction is always present. Sometimes we want friction. For example, friction between tires and the road allows a car to be steered safely and maintain its direction when moving. Other times we want to reduce friction. Putting oil on a bicycle chain reduces friction, allowing the chain to work more efficiently with the gears. This investigation explores different effects of friction.

Materials

- CPO Energy Car and Track (including the sled)
- CPO Physics Stand
- CPO DataCollector and 2 photogates
- Steel ball
- Tongue depressor
- Large paper plate
- Tape

1 Control setup

The first kind of friction you will be investigating is air friction. You will begin by finding out how a rolling car moves before you increase air friction.

Attach to the pole at the 7th hole.

Stop with no rubber band

Put 2 photogates somewhere on the track, with Photogate A first.

Photogate A

Photogate B

Clay ball (no rubber band)

1. Set up the track as a long, straight ramp as shown above.
2. Attach the track to the stand at the seventh hole from the bottom.
3. Place photogate A near the top of the track and photogate B near the bottom of the track.
4. Put a steel ball in the middle pocket of the car.
5. Let the car roll down the ramp, and record the time from A to B.
6. Measure the distance between the photogates.
7. Use the time and distance to calculate the average speed of the car.
8. Repeat two more times, for a total of three trials.
9. Calculate the average speed from your three trials.

Table 1: Control speeds

Trial	Time A to B (s)	Distance between A and B (cm)	Speed (cm/s)
1			
2			
3			
		Average Speed	

2 Create the "sail" car

A paper plate "sail" adds air friction (drag) to the system.

1. Tape a tongue depressor to the flag on the side of the car.
2. Tape a paper plate to the tongue depressor. Use enough tape to make sure it is securely attached.

3 Your hypothesis

a. Write a hypothesis that compares the speeds of the sail car and the normal car.

b. Explain your reasoning.

4 Do the investigation

1. Set up the track and photogates as in Part 1.
2. Put a steel ball in the middle pocket of the car.
3. Let the sail car roll down the ramp, and record the time from A to B.
4. Calculate the average speed of the car.
5. Repeat two more times, for a total of three trials.
6. Calculate the average speed from your three trials.

Table 2: Experimental speeds—sail car

Trial	Time A to B (s)	Distance between A and B (cm)	Speed (cm/s)
1			
2			
3			
		Average speed	

5 Analyzing and interpreting data

a. Did your results confirm your hypothesis? Explain.

b. How did air friction affect the car's motion?

6 Arguing from evidence

a. Friction is a force that opposes motion. Explain where the friction force on the sail comes from.

b. How could you increase the air friction on the car? How could you decrease it?

c. Is the sail the only source of friction? Do any other friction forces act on the car? Explain.

7 Setting up to measure rolling and sliding friction

Track setup

1. Set up the track so it is exactly level. Put a clay ball on the stopper at one end of the track. Attach a rubber band on the other end of the track, twisting it once so it makes an *X*. You will be using the rubber band to launch the car and sled.
2. Adjust the stopper near the launching end of the track so it is approximately 4 centimeters from the rubber band.
3. Place the sled on the track so the nose of the sled is touching the rubber band.
4. Place photogate A on the mark just ahead of the flag on the sled. The flag should not be blocking the photogate beam. Place photogate B 45 centimeters from photogate A.

8 Do the investigation

1. Launch the sled by resting your hand on the wooden track support and placing your index finger on the finger grip near the front of the sled. Practice a few times.

2. The sled should make it through both photogates. If it stops too soon, adjust the stopper so you can pull the rubber band back farther.
3. Record the time through each photogate and the time from photogate A to B.
4. Repeat for a total of three trials.

Table 3: Sliding friction data—sled

Trial	Time through A (s)	Time through B (s)	Time from A to B (s)	Speed through A (cm/s)	Speed through B (cm/s)	Acceleration (cm/s²)
1						
2						
3						
					Average acceleration	

5. The speed of the sled through photogate A is the width of the flag (1 cm) divided by the time through A. Calculate the speed through A. Repeat for photogate B.

6. Use the two speeds and the average time from A to B to calculate the acceleration. Then find the average acceleration for the three trials.

7. Repeat steps 3 through 6 using the car instead of the sled.

Table 4: Rolling friction data—car

Trial	Time through A (s)	Time through B (s)	Time from A to B (s)	Speed through A (cm/s)	Speed through B (cm/s)	Acceleration (cm/s²)
1						
2						
3						
					Average acceleration	

9 **Analyzing data**

a. Were your accelerations positive or negative? Why is this?

b. Which decelerated more, the sled or the car?

c. What does your answer question b tell you about the rolling friction of the car compared to the sliding friction of the sled?

d. Compare rolling friction, air friction, and sliding friction. Which do you think has the greatest effect on an object's motion? Which has the least effect?

Review the Design Steps from Chapter 2, page 50. The sail car you designed is a prototype. Redesign the sail car to increase the speed of the car by at least 5% or decrease the speed of the car by 5%. Document your evidence in data tables with images or videos. Obtain permission and a list of rules from your teacher. *Example*: The initial paper plate and tongue depressor must stay intact.

6A Newton's First and Second Laws

What is the relationship between force and motion?

The relationships between force and motion are known as Newton's laws. These are among the most widely applied relationships in all of physics. The first law explains what happens when there is *no* net force on an object, and the second law explains what happens when there *is* a net force. The two laws are closely related. We will focus in this investigation on what happens to the Energy Car's motion when you change the force and the mass separately. Both laws apply!

Materials

- CPO Energy Car and Track
- CPO DataCollector and 1 photogate
- 3 Same-size rubber bands
- 3 Steel marbles
- Electronic scale (or triple-beam balance)

1 Developing a model

Newton's second law explains what happens to the acceleration of an object when the force applied or the mass of the object is changed. For this part of the investigation, you will use different amounts of force to launch the car. You will not measure the resulting acceleration because you would have to measure it while the car is still being acted upon by the rubber band, and this is impossible. Instead, you will measure the *result* of the acceleration caused by the force of the rubber band. You can do this by looking at changes in the car's speed as it rolls along the track after the launch.

a. Make a prediction: What will happen to the speed of the car as the launch force increases?

2 Changing force with constant mass

Adjustment screw
1 rubber band (1st trial)
2 cm
1 marble
Square mark

Launching the car

Rest your palm on the wood, and pull the car against the screw with your finger on the tab on the far end of the car.

1. Set up the long, straight track with a rubber band on one end and a clay ball on the other end. Adjust the screw so the rubber band deflects about 2 centimeters. Be sure to stretch the rubber band once or twice before using.

2. Put one photogate on the first square mark after the rubber band.

3. Put one marble in the center of the car. Use the screw to launch the car with the same deflection of the rubber band each time. This means the same force is applied to each launch. Try to get three launches with times that are within 0.0015 seconds. Average these times and record the result in Table 1.

4. Repeat the experiment with two and three rubber bands. Stretch before using!

5. Calculate the car's speed. Remember to use the tab width (1.00 cm) for the distance.

Table 1: Changing force data

Number of rubber bands	Time through photogate (s)	Speed (cm/s)

3 Analyzing and interpreting data

a. During which portion of the car's motion is the rubber band affecting its speed?

b. Make a graph showing the speed of the car on the *y*-axis and the number of rubber bands on the *x*-axis. As the force was increased, what happened to the speed of the car?

c. Why was the same mass used for all trials (with different forces)?

4 Changing mass with constant force

Use 1 rubber band to launch cars with 0, 1, 2, and 3 marbles.

0 marbles

2 marbles

1 marble

3 marbles

1. Put a single rubber band on the launching end of the track. Stretch it before using. Leave the photogate in the same place (on the first square mark after the rubber band).

2. With the screw in the same place, launch cars of four different masses. Record the times through the photogate in Table 2.

3. Measure and record the mass of the car with zero, one, two, and three steel marbles.

4. Calculate and record each car's speed. Remember to use the tab width (1.00 cm) for the distance.

Table 2: Changing mass data

Mass of car (g)	Time through photogate (s)	Speed (cm/s)

5 Arguing from evidence

a. Use Table 2 to graph the speed of the car (*y*) against the mass (*x*). Does your graph show a direct relationship or an inverse relationship?

b. Why did the speed change when the same launch force was applied to cars of different mass? How do your observations support your answer?

c. Newton's first law is often called "the law of inertia." How does this law apply to the car's motion when you change the mass but keep the force constant?

d. Do you think the force applied to an object causes speed itself or causes changes in speed? Support your answer with at least one sentence of explanation.

When an object's speed changes, we say the object *accelerates*. Acceleration occurs whenever speed changes. To be precise, acceleration is the "change in speed divided by the change in time."

$$\text{Acceleration} = \frac{\text{change in speed}}{\text{change in time}}$$

e. Based on your collected data, propose a mathematical relationship between the variables *F* (force), *a* (acceleration), and *m* (mass).

6 Fun challenge

Try this additional mini-experiment. First, launch the car with one rubber band and no marbles. Then, launch the car with *two* rubber bands and *two* marbles. This means you will double both the force and the mass at the same time. How will the times compare? Make a prediction.

1. Launch the car with one rubber band and no marbles. Stretch the rubber band before using it. Get three times that are within 0.0015 seconds of each other and average. Record the time average in Table 3.

2. Launch the car with two rubber bands (be sure to stretch them first) and two marbles (placed in the front and the back of the car). Get three times that are within 0.0015 seconds of each other and average. Record the time average in Table 3.

Table 3: Doubling force and mass

	Time through photogate (s)
1 rubber band, no marbles	
2 rubber bands, 2 marbles	

a. What do you notice about the times?

b. Explain your result. How does it compare to your prediction?

6B Newton's Third Law

What happens when equal and opposite forces are exerted on a pair of Energy Cars?

When you apply a force to throw a ball, you also feel the force of the ball against your hand. That is because all forces come in pairs, called *action* and *reaction* forces. This is Newton's third law of motion. Every single force (action) has an opposite (reaction) partner. Action and reaction forces always act in opposite directions on two different objects. You can set up two Energy Cars to study Newton's third law.

Materials

- CPO Energy Car and Track
- CPO DataCollector and 2 photogates
- Rubber band
- 2 Steel marbles
- CPO Energy Car link
- Eyeglasses or safety glasses

1 Setting up and starting the investigation

1. Set up the long, straight track with a ball of clay on each stop. Use the bubble level to set the track level.
2. Place one steel marble in each car, and wrap one car with a rubber band.
3. Place two photogates 15 centimeters apart, as shown in the photo.
4. Place the two cars "nose to notch" between the photogates.
5. Squeeze the cars together, and attach them with the Energy Car link.
6. Center the attached car pair between the photogates so each is about to break the photogate's beam, but do not actually break the beam. Check that both photogate indicator lights are still green. Make sure all four wheels of both cars are on the track.
7. With a *very quick* upward motion, pull the link *straight up* and out from between the cars. ***Caution: Wear eyeglasses or safety glasses to avoid injury.***
8. Observe the time through each photogate. Repeat several times.

2 Constructing explanations

a. What caused the two cars to move when you removed the link?

b. According to Newton's third law, the cars experienced equal and opposite forces. How can you tell this is true by looking at the time through each photogate?

c. If one car was twice the mass of the other, would the cars still experience equal and opposite forces? Why or why not?

3 Changing the masses

Rubber band car

0 marbles

2 marbles

Four combinations

0 → 2
0 → 0
2 → 0
2 → 2

0 marbles

2 marbles

Note: Adding two steel marbles to the Energy Car doubles its mass.

1. Try the investigation with the four combinations of mass shown above. Take the average of three trials for each combination, and record your data in Table 1. *Caution: Wear eyeglasses or safety glasses to avoid injury.*

2. Calculate the average speed for each trial, and record in Table 1.

Table I: Energy Car action/reaction data

Marble pairings for connected cars		Time through photogate (s)		Speed (cm/s)	
A	B	A	B	A	B
0 marbles	2 marbles				
0 marbles	0 marbles				
2 marbles	0 marbles				
2 marbles	2 marbles				

4 Arguing from evidence

a. How does the speed of each car pair compare when masses are equal?

b. How does the speed of each car compare when one of the pair has twice the mass?

c. Explain how your speed data supports the idea that there are equal and opposite action and reaction forces acting on the cars.

d. If the action and reaction forces are equal in strength, when the cars separate, why does one car move at a different speed than the other when the masses are unequal? (*Hint*: The answer involves the second law of motion.)

7A Energy in a System

How is energy related to motion?

A system is a group of objects that interact with one another. Energy measures the ability of a system to change itself or other systems. This investigation explores systems and energy.

Materials

- CPO Energy Car and Track
- CPO DataCollector and 1 photogate
- Rubber band
- CPO Physics Stand

1 Making a system

1. Set up the track with a steep incline (hill) and a level section, as shown above.
2. Place a rubber band on the thumb screws at the bottom of the track.
3. Attach a photogate near the middle of the level section at the spot marked with a square.

2 Collecting data

1. Measure the distance between the center of the track and the stopper at the top of the track, as shown above. Record this distance (the drop position) in Table 1.
2. Hold the car against the stopper, and release it without giving it a push.
3. Record the time through the photogate before and after the car bounces off the rubber band. You will have to use the memory button to get the time before the bounce.
4. Calculate the speed of the car before and after it bounces. The speed is the width of the flag (1 cm) divided by the time it takes the flag to pass through the beam of the photogate. Record the speeds in the table.
5. Move the wooden track stop partway down the hill. Measure the distance from the center of the track to the metal stopper (the new drop position).

6. Release the car as you did before. Measure the times and calculate the speeds.
7. Repeat for several drop positions along the hill.

Table 1: Speed data

Drop position (cm from center)	Before bouncing		After bouncing	
	Time through photogate (s)	Speed (cm/s)	Time through photogate (s)	Speed (cm/s)

3 Constructing explanations

a. How high did the car climb up the hill after bouncing? Did it go higher, lower, or the same height as the drop position?

b. How is the drop position related to the speed of the car the first time it passes through the photogate (before bouncing)?

c. How do the speeds before bouncing compare to the speeds after bouncing? Is this the same for all five trials?

d. What could you do to make the car travel farther up the hill after bouncing?

e. In one paragraph, explain the answers to a, b, c, and d using the idea of energy.

7B Conservation of Energy

What limits how much a system may change?

A car launched up the hill at a given speed will never go higher than a certain point. A car rolling downhill will only reach a certain speed. Why? The answer is that nature keeps an exact balance of energy. Speed uses one form of energy, and height uses another. This investigation explores the exchange of energy.

Materials

- CPO Energy Car and Track
- CPO Physics Stand
- CPO DataCollector and 2 photogates
- Electronic scale (or triple-beam balance)
- Clay
- String
- Meter stick

1 Energy exchange from potential to kinetic

Drop the car from different position marks. Align the center of the car with the mark before releasing it.

Photogate goes here.

Stop (clay ball)   String

Photogate clamp

String through hole

Knot

Clamp with photogate

Measure height from the string to the center of the car.

The string is parallel to the straight section (level).

1. Set up the track with a hill and a level section. Make the level section as level as you can. Attach a photogate at the bottom of the hill on the level section.

2. Thread a string though the hole in the lower stop, and use a photogate to clamp the other end of the string to the stand. Adjust the string so it is parallel to the level section of the track.

3. Drop the car from each 5-centimeter mark on the hill, and measure the speed using the photogate time data. Measure the drop height of the car from the string to the center of the car.

Center of car

ENERGY car

4. Measure the mass of the car, and record it in Table 1.

Table 1: Height and speed data

Drop height (m)	Mass of car (kg)	Photogate time (s)	Speed (m/s)

2 Using your model

a. Graph the speed of the car vs. the drop height.

b. What does the graph tell you about the relationship between speed and drop height?

3 Arguing from evidence

a. Use the formula for potential energy to fill in the second column of Table 2.

b. Use energy conservation to derive a formula for the speed of the car in terms of the energy it has at the start. (*Hint*: Your formula should include only two variables, velocity and height.)

c. Use the formula you just derived to fill in the column for the predicted speed of the car.

d. Plot the curve for predicted speed on the graph you made in Part 2a above.

Table 2: Energy data and predicted speeds

Drop height (m)	Potential energy (J)	Predicted speed (m/s)	Measured speed from Table 1 (m/s)

4 Constructing explanations

a. Explain the relationship between speed and height using the concept of energy conservation.

b. Explain any difference between the predicted and measured speeds. If there is a difference, what does it tell you about the energy of the car as it rolls along the track?

c. Let the car roll downhill, bounce off the rubber band, and start back uphill again. Does the car reach the height it was dropped from? Explain why or why not using the concept of energy conservation.

d. Try this challenge. Use a rubber band to launch the car uphill so it goes through the photogate with the same speed as it had going down. You won't be able to get identical speeds, but come as close as you can. If the uphill and downhill speeds are the same, the car's kinetic energy is also the same in both directions. Does the car reach the same height on the hill that it was dropped from to get the same speed in Part 1? Explain any difference using the idea of energy.

8A Manipulating Forces

How do simple machines work?

Would you believe that a small child could lift an elephant? It can be done using a simple machine made out of ropes and pulleys. In this investigation, you will learn how to build machines that allow you to lift large weights with small forces. You will also learn how to measure the input and output forces of these machines.

Materials

• CPO Ropes and Pulleys kit
• Spring scales (2.5, 5, and 10 N)
• CPO Physics Stand

1 Setting up the ropes and pulleys

Throughout this investigation, you will be measuring forces with a spring scale. To get the most accurate readings, use a spring scale with the smallest maximum force needed. For example, using a 2.5-N scale to measure a force of 1 N will give you a more accurate result than using a 10 N-scale.

1. Attach four weights to the bottom pulley block. Use a spring scale to measure the weight of the bottom block. Record the weight of the bottom block: ____ N

2. The output force of this simple machine will be used to lift the bottom block. Attach the top block near the top of the Physics Stand. The yellow string can be clipped to either the top block or the bottom block. Start with the yellow string clipped to the bottom block.

Why all the strings?

• The yellow string will be used to move the bottom pulley block with the weights up and down. You will pull on one end of the yellow string. You will use the clip at the other end of the yellow string to attach the string to the pulley blocks.

• The yellow string may have several strands that directly support the bottom pulley block. These are called the supporting strands.

• The red string is the safety string. It holds up the bottom block while you rearrange the yellow string.

Safety Tip: Don't pull sideways or you can tip the stand over!

2 Investigating the ropes and pulleys

1. Clip the end of the yellow string to the bottom pulley block. Pass the string over the middle pulley of the top block. Use the marker stop (cord stop) to hook the spring scale to the string.

2. Measure the force it takes to slowly lift the bottom pulley block.

This arrangement has one supporting strand.

This arrangement has two supporting strands.

1. This arrangement has one strand supporting the bottom pulley block. Record the force in Table 1 in the row for one strand.

2. Unclip the yellow string from the bottom block, and pass it around the middle pulley in the bottom block as shown in the picture above. Clip the yellow string to the top block.

3. Move the marker, and measure the force it takes to slowly lift the bottom pulley block. Record this force in the row for two strands.

4. Rearrange the yellow strings so that you get three, four, five, and six supporting strands. Measure and record the force it takes to lift the bottom pulley block for each new setup.

Table 1: Force to lift pulley block

Number of supporting strands	Force to lift bottom pulley block (N)
1	
2	
3	
4	
5	
6	

a. As you add more supporting strands, what happens to the force needed to lift the bottom block?

b. How does the amount of input force required to lift the bottom block change with the string arrangement? Can you identify a mathematical rule?

3 Constructing explanations

a. How are all simple machines alike? How is a lever different from a machine made with ropes and pulleys? (Think about input and output force.)

b. What is the relationship between the number of strings on the ropes and pulleys and the amount of input force required to lift the bottom block?

8B Work

How can a machine multiply forces?

Simple machines such as ropes and pulleys and levers can create large output forces from small input forces. In this investigation, you will explore the nature of work and come to an interesting conclusion that is true for all machines.

Materials

- Top and bottom pulley block
- CPO Physics Stand
- 4 Weights
- Spring scale (0–10 N)
- Yellow string with clip and cord stop
- 2 Knobs (one threaded, one regular)
- Ruler

1 Setting up the investigation

Measuring the input force

1. Attach four weights to the bottom pulley block. Use a spring scale to measure the weight of the block in newtons. Record this value in column five of Table 1. This value is the *output force* and does not change in the experiment.

2. Using a ropes and pulleys set, clip one end of the yellow string to the bottom block. Pass the string over the middle pulley of the top block as shown.

3. Use the plastic cord stop to mark where the string leaves the top pulley.

4. Lift the bottom block a fixed height (h). The holes in the stand are 5 centimeters apart, so you can use the holes as a height reference. Use at least 20 centimeters as your lifting height.

5. Measure how much string length (L) you must pull to lift the block the chosen distance. You can measure this using the cord stops and a ruler.

6. Using the spring scale, measure the force needed to lift the block in newtons (N). This is the *input force*.

7. Record the input force, height difference for the block (h), and string length (L) in the first row of Table 1.

Measuring string length and height difference

8. Unclip the string from the bottom block, and clip it onto the underside of the top block. Pass the string around the middle pulley on the bottom block, and loop it up over the middle pulley of the top block, as shown. Pull the string to lift the bottom block the same height (h) that you used for the first setup. Measure the length (L) that you must pull the string. Record the values in the second row of Table 1.

9. Rearrange the yellow string so it passes over three, four, five, and six pulleys. You should always be pulling down on the string to raise the block, and you should always lift the bottom block the same height.

10. For each combination, record the input force and string length (L).

Table 1: Force and distance data

Number of pulleys	Height difference for block	String length	Input force	Output force (weight of block)	Work done on block (work output)	Work done by you (work input)
	(m)	(m)	(N)	(N)	(J)	(J)
1						
2						
3						
4						
5						
6						

2 Arguing from evidence

a. Calculate the work done on the block. This work is equal to the output force (weight of the block in newtons) times the height difference. The work done on the block should be the same for all configurations of the strings because the weight of the block and the height it was lifted did not change.

b. Next, calculate the work you did as you pulled on the string to lift the block in each trial. Your work is found by multiplying the input force by the string length.

c. As the number of supporting strings increased, what happened to the input force needed to lift the block?

d. As the number of supporting strings increased, what happened to the length of string that was pulled to raise the block?

e. As the number of supporting strings increased, what happened to the amount of work you had to do (work input) to lift the block?

f. Use your answers to the last three questions to explain the statement, "Nature does not give things away for free."

9A Levers

How does a lever work?

How could you lift a car—or even an elephant—all by yourself? One way is with a lever. A lever is a simple machine. What variables can you change when using a lever?

Materials

- CPO Lever
- CPO Physics Stand
- Steel weights
- String loops
- Short thumbscrew
- Knob

1 Setting up the lever

Hanging weights

Loop of string

Weights

Attaching the lever

Lever

Thumbscrew   Knob

Attaching the weights

1. Attach weights to hangers. You can put more than one weight on a single string.
2. Slide the loop of string through the hole in the weight.
3. Pull the knotted end through the loop, and tighten by pulling on the knot.
4. Slide a short thumbscrew through the hole in the middle of the lever.
5. Attach the lever to the Physics Stand by sliding the short thumbscrew through one of the holes on the front of the stand.
6. Use a knob to secure the lever and thumbscrew onto the back of the stand.
7. The knob should be tightened snugly on the thumbscrew and should press lightly against the back of the stand.
8. The weights can be hung from the lever by inserting the hanger key into the numbered key holes along the lever. The hanger key may also be clipped onto the top of the lever.

2 Levers in equilibrium

a. The lever is in equilibrium when all the weights on one side balance all the weights on the other side. Hang the weights as shown in step b. Does the lever balance?
   (*Note*: When the lever is in equilibrium, the lever arm is not necessarily perfectly horizontal.)

b. What variables can be changed to balance a lever?

1 weight   2 weights   4 weights

3 **Trying different combinations to balance the lever**

Make different combinations of weights and positions that balance. Use the chart below to write down the numbers of weights you put in each position. If you want to conduct more than four trials, draw your results on a separate sheet of paper.

50

4 Determine the mathematical rule for equilibrium

a. Draw a lever and label these parts: fulcrum, input arm, output arm, input force, and output force.

b. Using the data from the chart in Part 3, determine a mathematical rule for levers in equilibrium. Use these variables: input force, output force, length of input arm, and length of output arm. First, make some calculations; then, write your rule as an equation. The equation will have two variables on each side, with an equal sign in the middle.

5 Constructing explanations

a. Two ratios can be used to determine mechanical advantage in levers. What are the two ratios? What is the relationship between the two ratios?

b. What could you do to the input side of a lever to increase the amount of output force? (*Hint*: You could do two different things.)

9B Levers and the Human Body

What types of levers does your body have?

Your arms, legs, fingers, toes, jaw, and even your head and neck work like levers. Contracting and extending muscles provide the force to move your levers. Your joints are the fulcrums around which these levers pivot and move. Your bones are the levers themselves. In this investigation, you will look at the human arm and examine how it works like a lever.

Materials
- CPO Lever
- CPO Physics Stand
- Spring scales
- Steel weights

1 The human body

Let your left arm hang down by your side. Place your right hand into the inner part of your left elbow. Slowly lift your left arm (palm up) until it is level with the floor. Feel the tissue in your elbow tightening up with your right hand? That is the connective tissue that joins your biceps muscle to the bones of your forearm, the radius and ulna. You can use the Physics Stand and the lever to make a model of the human arm, and measure the forces involved when you lift something.

Attaching the lever

Attaching the weight and spring scale

Use what you have learned about lever terms to record your answers in the appropriate columns in Table 1. You will need to include units for each entry you record.

1. Attach the lever to the stand, but this time use the hole on the left-most side of the lever. Use one of the short thumbscrews. Do not tighten the knob all the way. Leave a little room so the lever can pivot.

2. Use a loop of string to hang one weight on the right-most side of the lever. Measure its weight in newtons using the green spring scale. Record the weight in Table 1.

3. Measure the distance in centimeters from the pivot point to the position of the hanging weight. Record the distance in Table 1.

4. Measure the distance from the pivot point to the next hole on the lever. This is where we will apply force to lift the lever. Record the distance in Table 1.

Table 1: Input and output data

Output force (N)	Input arm (cm)	Output arm (cm)	Mechanical advantage	Predicted input force (N)	Measured input force (N)

2 The lever arm model

a. Calculate the mechanical advantage of the lever. Record your result in Table 1.

b. Based on the mechanical advantage, predict the force required to lift the lever and keep it horizontal. Record your prediction in Table 1.

c. The connective tissue in your arm attaches your biceps to your forearm at the inside of your elbow. Since the muscle provides the lifting force close to the elbow joint, we will provide the lifting force for the lever close to the pivot point. Hook the red spring scale to the lever at the hole just to the right of the pivot point, and lift until the lever is horizontal. Keep it horizontal and record the force needed to keep it there in Table 1.

d. How does your predicted value compare to your measured value? Why do you think this is?

e. Test your reason why the values are different. What did you find?

f. Draw a diagram showing how the lever setup models an arm lifting a weight.

10A Pure Substance or Mixture?

How can observing the melting point identify a pure substance or a mixture?

Matter can be divided into two main categories: mixtures and pure substances. <u>Pure</u> <u>substances</u> are homogeneous throughout. They have the same chemical properties no matter where the sample is obtained or how large the sample is. <u>Mixtures</u> are combinations of two or more substances, with each substance retaining its chemical identity. In this investigation, you will obtain four test tubes containing unknown solids. You will measure the melting point, or the temperature at which the solid changes to a liquid, to determine if the matter is a mixture or a pure substance. Any given pure substance will always have the same melting point. Pure substances usually melt over a small temperature range, while mixtures often melt over a very wide temperature range.

Materials

- 4 Test tubes with unknowns
- Hot plate
- Stirring rod
- 250-mL Beaker
- Water
- Safety goggles
- Lab apron
- CPO DataCollector
- Temperature probe

> **WARNING** ── This lab contains chemicals that may be harmful if misused. Read cautions on individual containers carefully. Not to be used by children except under adult supervision.

1 Predicting

Why do you think a pure substance melts over a smaller range of temperatures than a mixture does?

2 Doing the investigation

1. Attach the temperature probe to the DataCollector, and set it to meter mode for the entire experiment. Record your sample label (A–D) in Table 1.

2. Add approximately 200 millileters of cold water to a 250-millileter beaker. Place the beaker on the hot plate, and turn the hot plate on to medium.

3. Place the first sample into the water bath, and have one group member hold the temperature probe about halfway in the water.

4. Another group member should stir the contents of the test tube with a stirring rod as it heats.

5. Watch the contents of the test tube carefully. At the moment the contents begin to melt, measure and record the temperature in Table 1.

Stirring rod
Test tube with sample
Temperature probe
Hot plate

6. Continue stirring the contents of the test tube and watching the contents until the entire sample is liquefied. Once the last solid particle melts, measure and record the temperature in Table 1.

7. Return your sample to your instructor.

8. Pour out the hot water in the beaker.

9. Repeat steps 2–8 for each of the remaining samples. Be sure to start with fresh cold water for each water bath.

Table 1: Melting data

Sample label	Temperature melting starts (°C)	Temperature melting ends (°C)
A		
B		
C		
D		

3 Arguing from evidence

a. How can you tell which test tubes contain pure substances and which contain mixtures?

b. If a sample contained 1 gram of pure substance A and another test tube contained 4 grams of pure substance A, how would the melting points differ? How would the experiment differ?

c. Name two possible sources of error for this experiment. How would they affect your data?

4 Constructing explanations

A white, waxy substance is heated in a test tube. Part of the substance melts almost immediately and is poured off into a seperate test tube after a minute of further heating, leaving a little more than half the original sample behind.

a. Explain why you think the original sample was a pure substance or a mixture.

b. Is the melted portion that was poured off a pure substance or a mixture? What evidence do you base your answer on?

c. Is the remaining portion left behind in the test tube a pure substance or a mixture? How could you find out for sure?

10B Determining Freezing/Melting Point

How do you determine the freezing/melting point of cetyl alcohol?

A cooling/heating curve is a plot of temperature versus time. It illustrates the effect on a substance as the temperature decreases/increases through a phase change. In this experiment, you will study the effects of cooling and heating cetyl alcohol through a phase chage. The data will be recorded using a DataCollector and then plotted on graphs. Based on your observations, measurements, and graphs you will be able to determine the freezing/melting point of cetyl alcohol.

Materials

- CPO DataCollector
- Temperature probe
- Test tube, 22 × 150 mm
- Cetyl alcohol
- Hot water
- Safety goggles
- Lab apron
- Heat-resistant gloves or hot mitts
- 250-mL Beaker
- 400–600-mL Beaker

1 Planning your investigation

WARNING — This lab contains chemicals that may be harmful if misused. Read cautions on individual containers carefully. Not to be used by children except under adult supervision.

a. The cetyl alcohol you will be using is a pure substance. What do you expect to observe in terms of the temperature range for the freezing/melting point?

b. Suppose your cetyl alcohol sample became contaminated with another substance. How would this affect the freezing/melting point?

2 Melting cetyl alcohol

1. Fill a 250-millileter beaker with cold water.
2. Fill a 400- to 600-millileter beaker with approximately 250 millileters of hot water (75–80°C).
3. Measure out approximately 4–5 grams of cetyl alcohol in a test tube.
4. Measure the temperature of the hot water to make sure it is within the range in step 2.
5. Quickly immerse the temperature probe into the cold water. Then remove and dry it making sure it is cooled to room temperature.
6. Set the DataCollector to data collection mode. Place the temperature probe into the test tube, and put the test tube containing the solid into the water bath. Press start on the DataCollector. View the experiment in graph mode.
7. Stir the solid vigorously with the temperature probe.

8. Continue to stir as long as some solid remains.

9. Once all of the material is liquid, stop and store the experiment. Record the experiment name assigned by the DataCollector in your notebook.

10. Leave the sample in the warm water for use in Part 4.

3 Make a prediction

a. Predict the effect of sample size on the melting/freezing point.

b. Describe and carefully sketch the shape of the graph from Part 2.

4 Freezing cetyl alcohol

1. Observe the cetyl alcohol in the test tube to make sure it is still all liquid. If some solid has formed, pour out the water in the warm beaker, and add more warm water.

2. Remove the test tube from the warm beaker and start a new experiment on the DataCollector.

3. Stir the liquid vigorously with the temperature probe as the solid begins to form.

4. Continue to stir until all of the liquid turns into a solid. (*Note*: If you need to repeat any part of the experiment, you may reuse your sample.)

5. When you are finished recording data, return your sample of cetyl alcohol to your teacher.

6. Record the experiment name assigned by the DataCollector in your notebook.

5 Using your model

a. Describe and carefully sketch the shape of the graph from Part 4.

b. Referring to both of your graphs, determine the melting and freezing point of cetyl alcohol. Are they the same? Should they be?

c. Based on the shapes of your curves, which data do you think is more reliable: the heating or cooling data? Why do you think so?

d. What is happening to the molecules of cetyl alcohol during the diagonal portions of the heating curve? What about during the plateau?

e. Your graph from Part 2 shows that during a change from solid to liquid, the temperature stays the same. Explain why the temperature does not increase, even though energy is being added.

11A Temperature and Heat

How are temperature and heat related?

Hot and cold are familiar sensations. What happens when something hot comes in contact with something cold? Think about putting some ice cubes in a drink. Things don't remain the same, changes occur, and these changes have to do with the movement of energy from one material to the other. This investigation will explore the difference between temperature and thermal energy, and how the movement of thermal energy relates to the concept of heat.

Materials

- Temperature probe
- CPO DataCollector
- Electronic scale (or triple-beam balance)
- Aluminum cube (from CPO Density Cubes kit)
- 3 12-oz foam cups
- Ice
- Cold and hot water
- Tongs
- 100-mL Graduated cylinder
- Safety goggles
- Lab apron

1 Making a prediction

Suppose you mix equal masses of water. One sample is at 0°C, and the other is at 50°C. What do you think the final temperature of the mixture will be? Why?

2 Mixing hot and cold water

1. You will need three 12-ounce foam cups for this experiment. Label two of the cups as follows: *HOT* and *COLD*.

2. Prepare an ice bath by placing approximately 250 millileters of water in the unlabeled cup and adding four or five ice cubes.

3. Connect the temperature probe to the DataCollector, and select meter mode for this experiment.

4. Place the temperature probe in the ice water bath.

5. Use a graduated cylinder to measure 100 millileters of very hot tap water. Pour the hot water into the cup labeled *HOT*.

6. Use a graduated cylinder to measure 100 millileters of the ice water. Pour the cold water into the cup labeled *COLD*.

7. Place the temperature probe into the cold cup. Wait until the reading stabilizes, then record the temperature in Table 1.

8. Place the temperature probe into the hot cup. Wait until the reading stabilizes, then record the temperature in Table 1.

9. Immediately pour the hot water into the cold water. This is the mixture.

10. Stir well using the temperature probe, and measure the final temperature (when it has stabilized). Record the temperature in Table 1.

11. Do not throw away your ice water. You will be using it again in the second part of the investigation.

Table 1: Temperature data for mixing equal masses of water

Cold water temp. (ºC)	Hot water temp. (ºC)	Mixture temp. (ºC)

3 Constructing explanations

a. Did the result of your experiment agree with your prediction (within 3ºC)? Discuss why the temperature value may have differed from your predicted value.

b. How do you think your results would have been different if you had used more hot water than cold water, instead of equal masses?

4 Making another prediction

a. Suppose you mix equal masses of cold water and hot metal. Will the temperature of the mixture follow the same pattern as the experiment you did in Part 2? Explain why you think so.

5 Combining hot metal and cold water

1. Find the mass of the aluminum cube, and record the mass in Table 2.
2. Connect the temperature probe to the DataCollector, and select meter mode.
3. Place the temperature probe in the ice water bath that was left from Part 2.
4. Place the aluminum cube in a foam cup, and cover it with very hot tap water. Let the aluminum cube stay in the hot water for several minutes so it gets warm.
5. Measure out a mass of water from the ice water bath that is equal to the mass of the aluminum cube, and pour it into a foam cup. Record the mass of the cold water in Table 2. Make sure there is no ice in the cup of cold water.
6. Move the temperature probe from the ice water bath to the cup of cold water, and record the temperature of the cold water in Table 2.
7. Record the temperature of the hot water and aluminum cube just before putting the cube in the cup of cold water. Record the temperature in Table 2.
8. Use the tongs to put the aluminum cube in the foam cup containing the cold water.
9. Stir the mixture with the temperature probe.
10. Record the temperature of the cold water and metal cube when the temperature has stabilized. Do not wait longer than 1 minute to measure the temperature. Record it in Table 2.

Table 2: Temperature data for combining water and metal

Metal mass (g)	Metal temp. before mix (ºC)	Cold water mass (g)	Cold water temp. before mix (ºC)	Mixture temp. (ºC)

6 Constructing explanations

a. Why didn't the temperature of the water and metal mixture measure halfway between the temperatures of the cold water and the hot aluminum cube, even though you mixed equal masses?

b. Explain what is happening between the aluminum cube and the water in terms of temperature and energy.

c. How much energy does it take to raise the temperature of 1 gram of aluminum 1°C compared to raising the temperature of 1 gram of water 1°C? (Look up this value.) Relate your answer to your experiment results. Do your results agree with other published findings?

d. Heat and temperature are related, but they are not the same. According to your results, what does the concept of heat take into account that temperature does not?

11B The Specific Heat of a Metal

How can you use specific heat to identify an unknown metal sample?

If you have ever walked barefoot on a concrete sidewalk on a hot and sunny day, you have felt its warmth on your feet. In fact, the thermal energy transferred to your feet from the concrete may send you running to the grass or even to a swimming pool. Why is the temperature of the concrete so different from the temperature of the grass or the pool water? Even though the sunlight shines on all three surfaces, it is easiest to raise the temperature of concrete. A hot, sunny day may only raise the temperature in a pool by 1 or 2 degrees. In this investigation, you will use a calorimeter, the specific heat of water, and the law of conservation of energy to determine the specific heat of a sample of copper and two unknown metal samples.

Materials

- CPO DataCollector
- Temperature probe
- 3 Foam cups (with or without lids)
- Electronic scale (or triple-beam balance)
- Metal samples (from CPO Density Cubes kit): copper and 2 unknown samples
- Hot water
- Tongs
- Safety goggles
- Lab apron

1 Doing the investigation

1. Place your sample of copper on the balance, and record its mass in Table 1.
2. Make a calorimeter by nesting two foam cups.
3. Pour about 150 millileters of room-temperature water into the calorimeter. Use the balance to measure and record the mass of the water you add to the calorimeter (density of water = 1g/mL). (*Note*: Make sure there is sufficient water in the calorimeter to submerge your metal sample *completely*.)
4. Fill a foam cup two-thirds full with hot water.
5. Place your sample of copper into the cup of hot water. Allow the copper sample to sit in the water for about a minute so it will get warm.
6. Use the temperature probe to measure the temperature of the hot water. When the temperature stabilizes, record it as the initial temperature of the metal in Table 1.
7. Place the temperature probe in the calorimeter. When the temperature stabilizes, record it as the initial temperature of the the water. Leave the temperature probe in the calorimeter.
8. Use the tongs to remove the copper from the hot water and to place it into the calorimeter. Try to transfer as little hot water as possible into the calorimeter. Move as quickly as possible, but do not spill any hot water.
9. Once the temperature stabilizes, record the final temperature of the mixture in Table 1.
10. Repeat steps 1–9 with each unknown metal provided by your teacher. You may be asked to conduct two trials with each of your unknown samples, if time allows.

Table I: Mass and temperature data

	Copper	Unknown metal #1	Unknown metal #2
Mass of metal sample (g)			
Mass of water in calorimeter (g)			
Initial temperature of water (°C)			
Initial temperature of metal (°C)			
Final temperature of mixture (°C)			

2   Processing the data

a. Calculate the temperature change of the water.

b. Calculate the temperature change of the metal.

c. Calculate the heat gained by the water using the equation below.

HEAT EQUATION

$$E = mC_p \, (T_2 - T_1)$$

Where E = thermal energy (Joules) lost or gained by the water in the calorimeter
m = original mass of the measured water in the calorimeter
C_p = specific heat of water (4.184 J/g°C)
$T_2 - T_1$ = change in temperature of the water (also referred to as ΔT)

d. The amount of energy released by the metal is equal to the amount of energy absorbed by the water. Knowing the value of E for the metal, calculate the specific heat (C_p) of the metal. (Remember, since the energy is being released by the metal, change the sign of E from + to −.)

e. Identify each unknown metal by comparing your calculated value of its specific heat to known specific heat values of common metals provided by your teacher.

f. Calculate the percent error for each unknown sample.

3 Constructing explanations

a. What did you determine were the identities of your unknown metals?

b. Looking at your data and the class data, were the experimental values too high or too low? Based on the experimental procedure, explain your observations.

c. How does the law of conservation of energy allow us to calculate the specific heat of a mystery metal?

d. The second unknown metal sample you tested is an alloy containing up to 80 percent of one of the other two metals you tested. The specific heat of this alloy should be almost the same as *one* of the other two metals. According to your results, which metal makes up 80 percent of the second unknown metal?

e. Water has a high specific heat. How does the fact that humans are made up largely of water help us regulate our body temperature?

12A Mystery Material

How do solids and liquids differ?

Review, in your mind, what you know about solids and liquids. You know, for example, that liquids do not keep their shape. They flow. Solids do not flow; they keep their shape. Consider the possibility of a material that is able to act like both a solid and a liquid. Could that be? In this investigation, you will not only consider the possibility but you will also actually play with such a material.

Materials

- Wax paper or small plastic bowls
- Mystery material

1 Doing the investigation

1. Your teacher will give you a sample of mystery material on a piece of wax paper or in a small plastic bowl.

2. Feel it. Smell it. Look at it. Use your senses to make as many observations as you can. Record your observations in Table 1.

Table I: Observations about the mystery material

I.	7.
2.	8.
3.	9.
4.	I0.
5.	II.
6.	I2.

2 Using your model

a. What happens when you squeeze the mystery material and when you release it?

b. How does the mystery material mimic some of the properties of solids and liquids?

c. The mystery material is made of only two ingredients—cornstarch and water. Using your answer from step a, what do you think is happening to the cornstarch and water when you squeeze and release it? Or when you hit it quickly or stick your finger slowly into it?

d. A colloidal suspension is a suspension of tiny particles of one substance in a medium of another substance. (The suspension remains intact indefinitely because it is unaffected by gravity.) Based on your observations and the definition, is the cornstarch and water mixture a colloidal suspension?

3 Constructing explanations

a. How is the cornstarch and water mixture similar to quicksand?

b. Why does a substance that acts like both a solid and a liquid seem unusual?

c. Can you think of any common material or product that might act like both a solid and a liquid?

12B Buoyancy

Can you make a clay boat?

A solid material will float if it is less dense than the liquid in which it is immersed, and it will sink if it is denser than the liquid. You may have noticed, however, that ships are often made of steel, which is obviously denser than water. So how does a steel ship float? In this investigation, you will experiment with modeling clay to discover how and why boats can be made of materials that are denser than water.

Materials

- Stick (or 1/2 stick) of clay
- Centimeter ruler
- Displacement tank
- 250-mL Beaker for overflow
- Water
- Paper towels, sponges
- 100-mL Graduated cylinder
- Balance
- Disposable cup to catch displaced water when refilling tank
- Dishpan or shallow bucket for testing clay boats
- Wax paper, for ease of cleanup

1 Measuring your stick of clay

Find the density of your stick of clay. Use a balance to measure its mass. Use the length × width × height method to calculate its volume. Record your measurements in Table 1.

Volume = length × width × height

Table 1: Mass, volume, and density of clay stick data

Length (cm)		Width (cm)		Height (cm)		Volume (cm³)
	×		×		=	Volume

Mass (g)		Volume (cm³)		Density (g/cm³)
	÷		=	

a. The density of water is 1 g/cm³. How does the density of your clay compare to the density of water?

b. Make a prediction: Will your stick of clay sink or float? Why?

2 Doing the investigation

A. Testing your model

Water level as high as possible without overflowing

Beaker for overflow water

1. Prepare the displacement tank for use. Place a cup or beaker under the spout to catch the overflow water. Fill the displacement tank until it just starts to overflow into the cup or beaker. Once it stops, remove the cup or beaker that was catching the overflow water.

2. Place a dry beaker under the spout to catch the overflow water displaced by your clay.

3. Gently put your stick of clay in the water. Does your stick of clay sink or float?

B. Finding the mass and volume of the displaced water

1. Pour the displaced water from the beaker into a 100-mL graduated cylinder. Record the volume in Table 2.

2. Now, calculate the mass of the displaced water using water's density and the volume of displaced water you measured. Record this value in Table 2.

C. Calculating the weight of your clay and the displaced water

Mass and weight measure two different properties of matter. Mass refers to how much matter the object contains. Weight measures the gravitational pull between the object and (in our case) Earth. The gravitational force between a 1-kilogram object and Earth is 9.8 newtons. So a 1-gram object's weight on Earth is 0.0098 newtons.

1. Use the mass of your clay to calculate its weight. Use the formula below and record the mass and weight in Table 2.

$$\text{mass in grams} \times (0.0098 \text{ N/g}) = \text{weight in newtons}$$

2. Calculate the weight of the displaced water. Use the formula above and record your data in Table 2.

Table 2: Mass and volume of clay and displaced water

	Mass of clay (g)	Weight of clay (N)	Volume of displaced water (mL)	Mass of displaced water (g)	Weight of displaced water (N)
Stick of clay					
Clay boat					

3 Challenge: Can you mold your clay into a shape that floats?

For this part of the investigation, you must mold *all* of your clay into a shape that you believe will float. Before you do, make a prediction:

How much water will the clay boat displace compared to the stick of clay?

1. When you are ready to test a shape, lower it into a container of water approximately three-quarters full. If the clay sinks, retrieve it immediately and dry it with a paper towel. Avoid mixing water into your clay, or it will get very slimy. Keep trying until you produce a boat that floats.

2. When you have successfully molded a boat that floats, take it out of the water and dry it with a paper towel. Then, prepare your displacement tank just as you did in step 2a.

3. Carefully place your boat into the displacement tank. Avoid making waves. When the water stops flowing, move the beaker away from the displacement tank spout. Safely remove a little water from the displacement tank so it doesn't overflow. Retrieve your boat and set it aside to dry.

4. Pour the displaced water from the beaker into a graduated cylinder. Record its volume in Table 2.

5. Use the density of water to calculate the mass of the displaced water. Calculate its weight using the formula from step 2, c1. Record both the water's mass and weight in Table 2.

6. When your boat is dry, measure its mass then calculate its weight using the formula from step 2, c1. Record both the mass and weight in Table 2.

4 Arguing from evidence

a. Did the weight of the clay change during the investigation? Why or why not?

b. Which displaced more water, the stick of clay or the clay boat? How much more?

c. Which weighed more, the stick of clay or the water it displaced? How much more?

d. Which weighed more, the clay boat or the water it displaced? How much more?

5 Why the boat floats

Use your mass and volume data from Table 2 to calculate the apparent density of your clay boat. This value is called the *apparent* density because the total volume of the floating boat is not displaced. The part of your floating boat that is above the surface isn't displacing any water. To find out how much of the boat is below the surface and *is* displacing water, look at the total amount of overflow water you measured.

Table 3: Data for boat

Mass of boat (g)	Volume of water displaced by the boat (mL)	Apparent density of the boat (g/mL)

6 Constructing explanations

a. Which displaced more water, the stick of clay or the floating clay boat?

b. Assuming that the mass of the clay did not change, how do you explain the difference in the volumes displaced by the stick of clay and the clay boat?

c. Look at the boat's apparent density. Why is it different from the density of the stick of clay? What other substance has a density very similar to the boat's apparent density?

d. Of all the properties you measured and calculated in this investigation, which one tells you the most about whether an object or material will float in water? How would you use that property to determine whether something will float?

e. Explain why a solid stick of clay sinks but a clay boat can be made to float.

f. What would happen if you added "cargo," like pennies, to your boat? Is there a limit to how much mass you can add before the boat sinks? Does the volume of displaced water increase or decrease when the boat gets heavier? Why? Try the experiment.

7 Engineering and the design cycle

a. The clay boat you made could be considered a "prototype" in the Engineering Design Cycle pictured at right.

b. Redesign your boat using other materials. The criteria are: the boat must float and hold a cargo of pennies.

c. Obtain permission and constraints from your teacher. (Example: The boat must fit in the displacement tank.)

d. Document evidence of the design changes and tests your boat undergoes in a series of numbered steps. Support your account with sketches, images, or videos.

13A Boyle's Law

How are the pressure and volume of a gas related?

Robert Boyle (1627–1691) conducted a series of experiments to investigate the physical properties of air. It was through these experiments that he discovered the relationship between the pressure and volume of an enclosed gas. Using a simple experiment, we will measure the pressure of a gas inside a syringe with a gas pressure sensor. You will use your data to derive the mathematical relationship between the pressure and volume of an enclosed gas at constant temperature.

Materials

- Gas pressure sensor
- CPO Gas Law kit
- CPO DataCollector

1 Thinking about pressure and volume

a. When you blow up a balloon, what happens to the volume of air inside the balloon?

b. What about the pressure? Does the pressure increase, decrease, or stay the same?

c. Now think about both pressure and volume together. Make a hypothesis about the relationship between pressure and volume of an enclosed gas. (*Hint*: When volume changes, what do you think happens to pressure?)

2 Setting up the investigation

1. Connect the 4-centimeter piece of tubing to the pressure sensor connector as shown.
2. Connect the other end of the tubing to the syringe.
3. Adjust the syringe until the volume of air is 12.0 millileters.
4. Screw the pressure sensor connector onto the pressure sensor.

| Connect tubing to pressure sensor connector. | Connect tubing to syringe. | Adjust syringe to 12 mL. | Screw pressure sensor connector onto pressure sensor. |

Connector Tubing

Tubing Syringe

5
10
12 mL
15
20
cc

Pressure sensor Connector

3 Doing the investigation

1. Start the DataCollector in data collection mode. Record the pressure at 12.0 millileters (in kPa) in Table 1.

2. Pull the syringe out until it measures 16.0 millileters. Hold it until the pressure stabilizes. Again, record the pressure in Table 1.

3. Repeat step 3 for volumes of 18.0 millileters and 10.0 millileters.

4. Repeat step 3 with a volume of 6.0 millileters. However, take the measurement quickly to prevent air from escaping.

5. Stop the DataCollector. Do not disconnect the syringe from the sensor yet.

Table 1: Pressure and volume data

Volume (mL)	Pressure (kPa)	P · V (kPa · mL)	P/V (kPa/mL)
6.0 mL			
10.0 mL			
12.0 mL			
16.0 mL			
18.0 mL			

4 Graphing your data

a. Use your data to make a graph of pressure vs. volume.

b. Does the graphical model support your hypothesis? Explain your answer.

c. What happens to the pressure of an enclosed gas when the volume increases?

5 Finding a relationship between pressure and volume

a. Multiply the pressure and volume values for each trial, and record the values in the third column of Table 1. Remember to use the correct number of significant digits.

b. Divide the pressure by the volume for each trial, and record the values in the last column of Table 1. Again, use the correct number of significant digits.

c. Boyle's law states that there is a mathematical relationship between pressure and volume that always equals a constant value. Based on your calculations, is that relationship $P \times V$ or P/V?

d. According to your data, what is the constant value? How well does this agree with Boyle's law?

6 Using Boyle's law to make a prediction

a. Using your constant value, calculate the pressure when the volume of the syringe is set to 14.0 millileters.

b. Using your graph, what pressure corresponds to 14.0 millileters? How does this compare to your calculated value?

c. Test your predicted pressure value for 14.0 millileters. How do the values compare?

13B Pressure and Temperature Relationship

How are the temperature and pressure of a gas related?

Gas molecules are in constant motion. When the temperature of a gas increases, the molecules move faster. When this happens, the velocity and number of molecular collisions also increase. The opposite is true for a gas when the temperature of a gas decreases. In this investigation, you will study the relationship between the pressure a gas exerts and the temperature of the gas.

Materials

- Gas pressure sensor
- Single-hole rubber stopper/tube assembly
- Temperature probe
- CPO DataCollector
- 125-mL Erlenmeyer flask
- CPO Displacement Tank
- Cold water
- Hot water
- Safety goggles

1   Thinking about temperature and pressure

a. Car manuals tell you to inflate the tires to a certain pressure in cold weather before driving around on them. Why do you think this is important?

b. Make a hypothesis about the relationship between the pressure and temperature of an enclosed gas. (*Hint*: When temperature increases, what do you think happens to the pressure?)

2   Setting up the investigation

1. Fill the displacement tank with ice- cold water to the 1,200-millileter mark.
2. Place a temperature probe in the water, and connect the probe to the DataCollector. The water temperature should be about 10–12°C, but any cold starting temperature will work.
3. Place the rubber stopper/tube assembly into the 125-mL Erlenmeyer flask. Attach the pressure sensor to the tube.
4. Connect the pressure sensor to the DataCollector.

Temperature probe — Single-hole rubber stopper — Pressure sensor — Erlenmeyer flask — Displacement tank filled to 1,200-mL mark

3 Doing the investigation

1. Place the flask into the cold water bath, and allow it to sit for 2 minutes. Record the temperature and pressure in Table 1 after 2 minutes have passed.
2. Take the flask out of the water. Use a container to remove 400 millileters of water from the displacement tank.
3. Get 400 millileters of hot water from your teacher, and pour it into the displacement tank.
4. Place the flask into this warmer water. After it has been in the water for 2 minutes, record the temperature and pressure in Table 1.
5. Repeat steps 2–4 two more times so you have a total of four data points.
6. Convert Celsius temperatures to Kelvin, and record in Table 1.

Table 1: Pressure and temperature data

Pressure (kPa)	Temperature (°C)	Temperature (K)	P/T (kPa/K)	P · T (kPa · K)

4 Graphing your data

a. Use your data to make a graph of pressure vs. temperature.

b. Does the graphical model support your hypothesis? Explain your answer.

c. What happens to the pressure of an enclosed gas when the temperature increases?

5 Finding a relationship between pressure and temperature

a. Divide the pressure and temperature values for each trial, and record the answers in the fourth column of Table 1. Remember to use the correct number of significant digits.

b. Multiply the pressure by the temperature for each trial, and record the values in the last column of Table 1. Again, use the correct number of significant digits.

c. The mathematical relationship between pressure and temperature always equals a constant value. Based on your calculations, is that relationship P/T or P × T?

d. According to your data, what is the constant value?

6 **Using the pressure–temperature relationship to make a prediction**

a. Using your constant value, calculate the pressure of the air in the flask when the temperature is 333 K.

b. Using your graph, what pressure corresponds to 333 K? How does this compare to your calculated value?

c. How would you use the investigation setup to test your predicted pressure value for 333 K?

7 **Constructing explanations**

a. You used a water bath to change the temperature of the air in the flask. Draw a diagram of the investigation setup, and use arrows to show the heat transfer that took place when more and more hot water was added to the displacement tank.

b. What two factors in the experiment were constant?

c. Go back to your answer to question 1a. Would you answer the question the same way now? Explain.

14A The Atom

What is inside an atom?

We once believed that atoms were the smallest units of matter. Then scientists discovered even smaller particles inside atoms! The structure of the atom explains why nearly all the properties of matter we experience are what they are. This investigation will lead you through some challenging and fun games that illustrate how atoms are built from protons, neutrons, and electrons.

Materials

• CPO Atom Building Game

1 Modeling an atom

In the atom game, colored marbles represent the three kinds of particles. Red or green marbles are protons, blue marbles are neutrons, and yellow marbles are electrons.

Build the atom above using three red or green, three blue, and three yellow marbles.

2 Using your model

a. What is the number below the element symbol called? What does this number tell you about the the atom?

b. What is the number(s) above the element symbol called? What does this number(s) tell you about the atom?

c. Why do some elements have more than one number above the symbol? What are the variations in this number called?

3 Making atoms

Build the six atoms shown on the chart, and fill in the missing information. Protons and neutrons go in the middle of the board. Electrons go around the outside and fill up the holes from the lowest row to the highest.

	Element	Atomic number	Mass number	Protons	Neutrons	Electrons
3a				●●●●	○○○○○	
3b				●●●●●●	○○○○○○	
3c					○○○○○○○○	○○○○○○
3d		8			○○○○○○○○	
3e				●●●●●●●●●●	○○○○○○○○○○	○○○○○○○○○○
3f			27	●●●●●●●●●●●●●		

4 Analyzing and interpreting data

a. Two of the atoms you made are the same element. What is different about them?

b. One of the atoms has just enough electrons to completely fill the first two rows. Which atom is this? Where on the periodic table is it found?

c. Which atom has an atomic number of 8?

d. Which atom has a mass number of 14?

e. One atom is found in a lightweight, silvery metal used in airplanes. Which atom is it?

f. Which atom represents an element that makes up about 21 percent of the air you breathe? You could not live without this element.

Periodic Table of the Elements 1- 54

(Stable isotopes)

Element Symbol
Atomic Number

Key

Stable Mass Numbers

14B Atomic Challenge!

How were the elements created?

During the Middle Ages, people believed you could turn lead into gold if you followed the right procedures. Later, we learned that lead and gold are different elements with different kinds of atoms. You have to change the atoms inside to turn lead into gold. Lead atoms have 82 protons in the nucleus. Gold atoms have 79 protons.

Materials

* CPO Atom Building Game

1 Building the elements

About 13 billion years ago, when the universe was much younger, the only atoms in existence were hydrogen, helium, and a small amount of lithium. These are the three lightest elements. Today, we find carbon, oxygen, iron, and even uranium atoms in nature. Where did these heavy atoms come from? All of the elements were created in the super-hot cores of stars. Stars get their energy by combining hydrogen atoms to make other elements, such as helium. Along the way, a few protons get converted to neutrons and electrons, too.

2 Quick review of the atom

In the atom game, colored marbles represent the three kinds of particles. Red or green marbles are protons, blue marbles are neutrons, and yellow marbles are electrons.

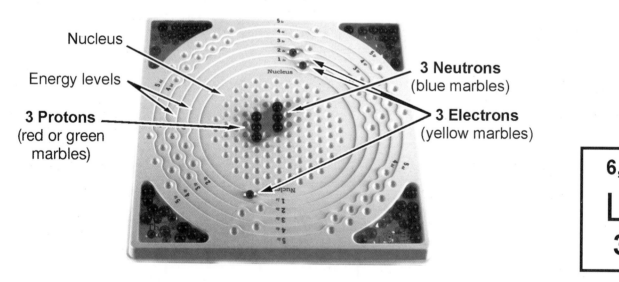

The Three Rules

Rule 1: The number of protons matches the atomic number.

Rule 2: The total number of protons and neutrons equals a stable mass number.

Rule 3: The number of electrons matches the number of protons.

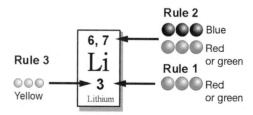

3 The game of Atomic Challenge

This game simulates how the heavy elements were created inside stars. Each player takes a turn adding protons, neutrons, and electrons to the atom to build heavier and heavier elements.

1. The winner of the game is the first player to use all of his or her marbles.

2. Each player starts with six blue marbles (neutrons), five red or green marbles (protons), and five yellow marbles (electrons).

3. Each player takes turns adding one to five marbles, but not more than five. The marbles may include any mixture of electrons, protons, and neutrons.
    For example: you can add one blue, one red or green, and one yellow marble in a turn. That makes three total marbles, which is less than five.

4. Marbles played in a turn are added to the marbles already in the atom.

5. Only atoms in which the combination of electrons, protons, and neutrons matches one of the naturally occurring elements on the periodic table are allowed. If you add marbles that make an atom *not* on the red periodic table, you have to take your marbles back and lose your turn.

6. A player can trade marbles with the bank *instead* of taking a turn. The player can take as many marbles (of as many colors) as they need, but must take at least as many total marbles as they put in. For example, a player can trade two yellows for one yellow, one blue, and one red or green.

Example of a good move

$$Li^7 + p + n + e = Be^9$$

4 Constructing explanations

Atoms that are not on the periodic table shown may exist in nature, but they are radioactive and unstable. For example, carbon-14 (C^{14}) is unstable and is not listed, but carbon-12 (C^{12}) and carbon-13 (C^{13}) *are* stable and *are* on the table.

a. What four elements make up almost all the mass in the human body?

b. How many stable isotopes does oxygen have?

c. Find one element on the table that has no stable isotopes.

d. What element has atoms with 26 protons in the nucleus?

e. On most periodic tables, a single atomic mass is given instead of the mass numbers for all of the stable isotopes of an element. How is this mass related to the different isotopes?

15A The Periodic Table

How is the periodic table organized?

Virtually all the matter around us is made up of combinations of elements. Scientists know of 118 different elements, of which about 90 occur naturally. Each element has its own unique kind of atom. The periodic table is a chart that shows all of the elements in order of increasing atomic number.

Materials

- CPO Periodic Table Tiles

1 Building the periodic table

Every element is represented by a symbol made up of one or two letters. For example, the symbol for hydrogen is a capital letter *H*. The symbol for lithium is two letters, Li. Each element also has a unique number, called its atomic number. The *periodic table* is a chart that shows the elements in an arrangement that helps us recognize groups of elements with similar properties. The picture below shows the shape of the periodic table and the first few elements in sequence from left to right. The elements are arranged from lowest to highest atomic number.

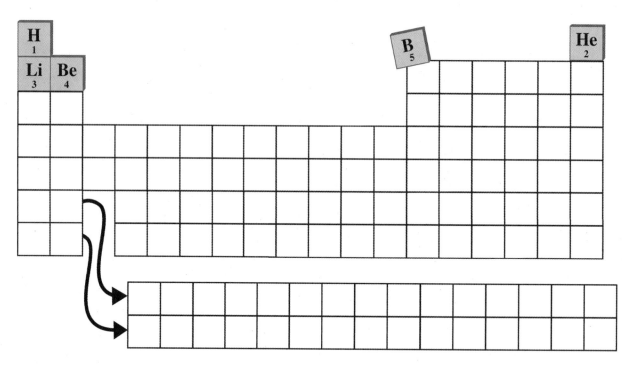

Using the chart as a guide, build the periodic table out of the Periodic Table Tiles. The only tile you should use yellow-side up is the hydrogen tile. When you are finished, the colors will show a pattern. There is a tricky part near the bottom of the table. The table breaks off between element 56 (Ba) and element 71 (Lu), and fills in the first of two long rows underneath the main part of the chart.

2 Organization of the periodic table

Look at the periodic table you put together out of the tiles. Use the diagram below and your model of the periodic table to answer the questions.

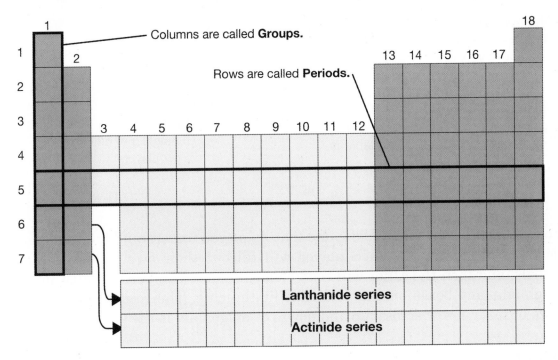

Groups 1–2 and 13–18 are the main group elements. Groups 3–12 are the transition metals.

a. Which elements are in group 1?

b. Which elements are in group 8?

c. Name three transition metals.

d. To which group does chlorine belong? What other elements are in that group?

e. Which elements are in the 2nd period?

3 Arguing from evidence

a. Each row (period) of the periodic table contains only a certain number of elements. What does this number have to do with the structure of the atom? Research this question in your textbook.

b. Which group of the periodic table above contains the element argon? What characteristic do the elements in this group share?

c. Which group contains the element carbon? What characteristic do the elements in this group share?

15B Periodic Table Challenge

What information can you get from the periodic table?

Each box on the periodic table tells you the element symbol, atomic number, and atomic mass for all the known elements. This alone is very useful information, but did you know that the arrangement of the elements on the periodic table gives you even more information? Each major column of elements represents a group of elements with similar chemical behavior. Can you see why the arrangement of elements on the periodic table is important?

Materials

- Blank periodic table bingo card sheets; 1 per player
- Caller's clues and checklist; 1 per team
- Copy of the periodic table of elements; 1 per player
- Highlighter or other marker; 1 per player

1 The challenge

Periodic Table Challenge is a bingo-like game that helps you understand how the elements on the periodic table are arranged. Each player will fill out their own five-by-five grid with element symbols, and then the caller will read element clues. The players must interpret the clues and highlight any boxes on the grid that fit the clue. The first player who correctly highlights five boxes in a row across, up and down, or diagonally is the winner.

2 Rules of play

1. Designate one member of your group to be the caller. The caller will call out clues and keep track of them on the checklist.

2. Each player will have four blank grids. Fill out one of the grids with random element symbols (other grids can be used for additional games). You may choose elements in the atomic number range of 1–54 (hydrogen through xenon). Do not repeat symbols on the card. You will only be able to fit 25 of the possible 54 symbols on the card. You choose which ones to use and where to place them on the grid.

3. The caller will randomly pick and call out clues from the list. As a clue is called out, the caller will check it off. The possible answers are only for the caller to confirm the winning card.

4. When a clue is read, players check their grid to see if any of the elements fit the clue. Any elements that fit the clue must be highlighted. If no elements fit the clue, then no boxes are highlighted on that turn.

5. When a player has highlighted five boxes in a row up and down, across, or diagonally, play stops. The caller will double-check the clue list and answers to see if the clues indeed match the highlighted elements. If they do not, play continues until a true winner is determined.

3 Caller's clues

You can call clues in any order. Check off each clue as you use it.

Clue	Possible answers
A member of the carbon group	C, Si, Ge, Sn
Chemical properties similar to calcium, but not calcium	Be, Mg, Sr
A transition metal that has a "C" in the symbol	Sc, Cr, Co, Cu, Tc, Cd
A member of the oxygen group	O, S, Se, Te
Chemical properties similar to cesium, but not cesium	H, Li, Na, K, Rb
A member of the noble gas group	He, Ne, Ar, Kr, Xe
A nonmetal in the nitrogen group	N, P
A metal in the boron group	Al, Ga, In
A gas in the oxygen group	O
A solid in the halogen group	I
An element that is liquid at room temperature	Hg, Br
A transition metal with less than 25 protons	Cr, V, Ti, Sc
A transition metal commonly found in jewelry	Ni, Cu, Ag
A metalloid in the carbon group	Si, Ge
Chemical properties similar to aluminum, but not aluminum	B, Ga, In
A transition metal with 39–43 protons	Y, Zr, Nb, Mo, Tc
An element symbol with a first letter that is different from the first letter of the name	Na, K, Fe, Ag, Sn, Sb
A member of the nitrogen group with a one-letter symbol	N, P
A transition metal from the 5th period	Y, Zr, Nb, Mo, Tc, Ru, Rh, Pd, Ag, Cd

4 Periodic table challenge card

Fill in each square with the symbol of an element having an atomic number between 1 and 54 (hydrogen–xenon).

Do not use the same element symbol more than once.

16A Chemical Bonds

Why do atoms form chemical bonds?

Most of the matter on Earth is in the form of compounds. Even when a substance exists as a pure element, it tends eventually to combine with other elements. For example, if you leave an iron nail outside in the rain, it will quickly combine with the oxygen in the air to form iron oxide, better known as rust. In this investigation, you will build models of atoms and discover one of the fundamental concepts in chemistry: the role of electrons in the formation of chemical bonds.

Materials

- CPO Atom Building Game

1 Reviewing atomic structure

The electrons fill from the bottom up:

then these
next these
first these
nucleus

Let's review what you already know about atoms:

- A neutral atom has the same number of electrons and protons.

- The electrons occupy energy levels surrounding the nucleus.

- Since electrons are attracted to the nucleus, they fill the lower energy levels first.

- Once a given level is full, electrons start filling the next level.

2 How many electrons in the outermost level?

Using the Atom Building Game, build each element in Table 1. For each element, record the number of electrons and the number of unoccupied spaces in the outermost energy level

Table 1: Element data

Element	Atomic number	Electrons in outermost level	Unoccupied spaces in outermost level
Hydrogen			
Helium			
Lithium			
Fluorine			
Neon			
Sodium			
Chlorine			
Argon			
Potassium			

3 What are valence electrons?

Examine Table 1 and answer the following questions.

   a. According to your textbook, what are *valence electrons*?

   b. What do lithium, sodium, and potassium have in common?

   c. What do fluorine and chlorine have in common?

   d. What do neon and argon have in common?

4 Modeling a chemical bond

Atoms that have a complete outermost energy level are stable. If there are empty holes, an atom will either gain, lose, or share electrons with another atom in order to fill these holes. In doing so, the atom completes its outermost level and becomes stable. When an atom gains, loses, or shares electrons with another atom, a *chemical bond* is formed.

Using two Atom Building Games, build a sodium atom and a chlorine atom. Put them next to each other, then answer the questions below.

   a. In order to complete its outermost energy level, do you think sodium will tend to lose its only valence electron or gain seven? Explain your answer.

   b. In order to complete its outermost energy level, do you think chlorine will tend to lose all seven of its valence electrons or gain one? Explain your answer.

   c. Why might these two atoms bond together to form a molecule? In your answer, describe what you think might happen when sodium and chlorine form a chemical bond.

5 Determining oxidation numbers

An element's <u>*oxidation number*</u> is equal to the charge an atom has when it *ionizes*—that is, when it gains or loses electrons.

Use your models of sodium and chlorine to answer the following questions.

a. Remove the valence electron from sodium. What has happened to the balance of positive and negative charges? What is sodium's oxidation number?

b. Move the electron you took from sodium to chlorine. What happens to chlorine's charge when it gains the electron from the sodium atom? What is chlorine's oxidation number?

c. When sodium and chlorine form a chemical bond, what is the overall charge of the molecule? Why do you think sodium and chlorine combine in a 1:1 ratio?

6 Modeling chemical bonds

Use multiple atom boards for this part of the investigation. First, build each atom. Next, move the boards together to model the formation of a chemical bond.

a. one carbon atom and four hydrogen atoms

b. two lithium atoms and one oxygen atom

c. one beryllium atom and two fluorine atoms

7 Using models

a. – c. Read about Lewis dot diagrams in your textbook. Draw a dot diagram for each compound in Part 6.

16B Chemical Formulas

Why do atoms combine in certain ratios?

Chemists have long noticed that elements in the same group behave similarly. The periodic table is an arrangement of the elements grouped according to similar behavior. In this investigation, you will discover how the arrangement of electrons in atoms is related to groups on the periodic table. You will also learn why atoms form chemical bonds with other atoms in certain ratios.

Materials

- CPO Periodic Table Tiles
- Periodic table with oxidation numbers
- Special Bonds cards

1 Oxidation numbers and ions

An element's *oxidation number* indicates how many electrons are lost or gained when chemical bonding occurs. The oxidation number is equal to the charge an atom has when it *ionizes,* or gains or loses electrons to become an *ion*. The partial periodic table below shows the most common oxidation numbers of the main group elements. The oxidation numbers are written above each column, or group, on the table.

Oxidation Numbers from the Periodic Table

NOTE: Many elements have more than one possible oxidation number.

2 Analyzing and interpreting data

a. How is an element's group related to the number of valence electrons in its outermost level?

b. Why do elements in group 2 have an oxidation number of 2+?

c. Why do elements in group 17 have an oxidation number of 1–?

d. Why do the oxidation numbers in the first two groups tend to be positive?

3 Predicting chemical formulas

A _binary compound_ is composed of two different elements. Predict the chemical formulas for the binary compounds that are made up of the pairs of elements in Table 1. Use the following steps.

1. Using the periodic table in Part 1, determine the ion formed by each element. Record the oxidation numbers.
2. Figure out how many Periodic Table Tiles of each element will be needed to make the compound electrically neutral.
3. Form the compound with your tiles, and write the chemical formula for each compound based on the number of tiles of each element.

Table 1: Writing chemical formulas for binary compounds

Element 1	Element 2	Oxidation no. 1	Oxidation no. 2	Number of tiles of element 1	Number of tiles of element 2	Chemical formula
Hydrogen	Fluorine					
Magnesium	Sulfur					
Calcium	Bromine					
Aluminum	Oxygen					
Potassium	Chlorine					
Lithium	Argon					
Rubidium	Sulfur					

4 Naming compounds

Naming binary ionic compounds is very simple if you follow these rules.

1. Write the name of the element with a positive oxidation number first.
2. Write the root name of the element with a negative oxidation number second. For example, *chlor-* is the root name of chlorine. Subtract the *-ine* ending to get the root.
3. Add the ending *-ide* to the root name. *Chlor-* becomes *chloride*.

Using these rules, write the name of each compound in Table 1.

5 Playing Compound Crossword

Now that you understand how elements combine to form compounds, you are ready to play Compound Crossword. In this game, you will score points by forming stable compounds, crossword style. Players use the oxidation numbers of the elements to form correct compounds. Points are determined by adding up the atomic numbers of each atom in the compound.

Sample game after four turns

CH_3OH scores 18 points.

Fe_2O_3 scores 76 points.

SiO_2 scores 30 points.

H_2SO_4 scores 50 points.

Starting the game

Each player starts with 10 randomly selected tiles. The remaining tiles should be placed in a box or paper bag so they may be drawn without being seen. The playing surface can be any flat table (or floor) with minimum dimensions of 75×75 centimeters.

Each player draws a tile from the bag; the highest atomic number goes first. Once the starting player has been determined, those tiles are returned to the bag. The play continues to the starting player's right.

Play

1. Players take turns adding a compound to the crossword by using tiles from their set of 10. Either side of a tile may be used.
2. The elements in a compound may be arranged in any order as long as they are in a single horizontal or vertical row.
3. Each new compound played must have oxidation numbers that add up to zero. Otherwise, the player must take back the compound and wait until his or her next turn.
4. If the compound is correct, the player adds up the atomic numbers of all the atoms in the compound to determine the points and then draws new tiles to restore a set of 10.

5. Play continues until all the tiles in the bag are used and one player is out of tiles, or until no player is able to make a compound.

6. The winner is the player with the highest score at the end of the game.

Determining correct compounds

The oxidation numbers found directly above each element on the periodic table provided are used to determine whether a molecule is correct. The oxidation numbers of all the elements in the compound must add up to zero. In some cases, there is more than one oxidation number for an element. Iron (Fe), for example, has oxidation numbers of +2 and +3. The player may use either oxidation number when calculating.

The Special Bonds card included with the Periodic Table Tiles gives some additional possibilities for forming compounds.

Examples of correct and incorrect compounds

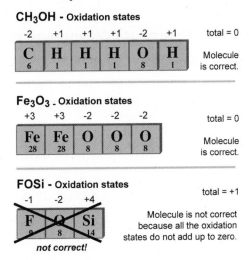

The oxidation number for each element in a compound is counted once for every atom of that element present. The two iron atoms contribute a total of +6, which is balanced by the −6 from the three oxygen atoms.

Note: The Special Bonds card offers some extra ways that compounds can form when two atoms of the same element bond together, and when hydrogen is involved in unusual ways. The example of CH_3OH (methanol) above uses one of the special bonds that hydrogen can make with carbon.

Miscellaneous rules and strategies

The noble gases do not form bonds and therefore can't be played. Players may decide at the start of the game to remove these tiles. As another option, players can choose to turn the noble gas tiles over, revealing the + symbol. This tile could then be used as a wild card that allows the player to choose which element the + should represent. This wild card scores no points but allows the player to complete a molecule. Players must agree on the use of the noble gas tiles before the Compound Crossword game begins.

17A Chemical Equations

How are atoms conserved in a chemical reaction?

A chemical reaction involves changes in substances that react to form new substances. This process involves the breaking of chemical bonds and the formation of new ones. A chemical equation shows the chemical formulas of the substances that react, called reactants, and the chemical formulas of the substances that are produced, called products. The number and type of atoms in the reactants must be exactly equal to the number and type of atoms in the products. How do you write a chemical equation so that the numbers and types of atoms on the reactants and products sides are balanced?

Materials

• CPO Periodic Table Tiles

1 Writing chemical equations

Magnesium metal reacts with water to produce magnesium hydroxide and hydrogen gas.

The statement above is the word form of a chemical reaction. It tells you the names of the reactants and the products. To write it as a chemical equation, you need to determine the chemical formulas of each of the substances in the reaction.

1. Magnesium metal is an element and exists as an atom. Its chemical formula is Mg.

2. The chemical formula for water, a compound of hydrogen and oxygen, is H_2O.

3. Magnesium hydroxide is an ionic compound. To write its chemical formula, you need to find out the charges of each ion it is made of. The magnesium ion is Mg^{2+}. The hydroxide ion is OH^-. You need 1 Mg^{2+} and 2 OH^- to make a neutral compound, so the formula is $Mg(OH)_2$.

4. Pure hydrogen gas always exists as a diatomic molecule, so its chemical formula is H_2.

The chemical equation is written as follows:

magnesium metal	reacts with	water	to produce	magnesium hydroxide	and	hydrogen gas
Mg	**+**	H_2O	⟶	$Mg(OH)_2$	**+**	H_2

2 Trying out the reaction with Periodic Table Tiles

Use Periodic Table Tiles to make the reactants above.

Rearrange the reactants to make the products. Is there any problem? What are you missing?

3 Balancing the reaction

Chemical equations must always balance. This means that you must use all of the atoms you start with and you cannot have any leftover atoms when you are finished. If you need more atoms to make the products, you can only add them in the form of a chemical formula.

You cannot simply add the extra atoms that you need unless the chemical formula is a single atom—like Mg. Which atoms did you need more of for the reaction you tried? Since you needed more oxygen and hydrogen atoms, you can only add them in the form of another water molecule. Try adding another water molecule to the reactants and rearranging them to form the products again. Did the equation balance this time?

4 Writing balanced chemical equations

To balance the equation for this reaction, you needed to add one more water molecule to the reactants side to get the correct amount of products. Since one magnesium atom reacts with two water molecules to form one magnesium hydroxide molecule and one hydrogen diatomic molecule, the proper way to write the balanced chemical equation is

$$Mg + 2H_2O \longrightarrow Mg(OH)_2 + H_2$$

The *2* in front of H_2O is called a coefficient. This number tells you how many water molecules are needed in the reaction. The rest of the reactants and products in the reactants show no coefficients. This is because when the coefficient is *1*, there is no need to write it.

5 Try balancing these chemical equations

The following chemical equations have the correct reactants and products. Balance each equation using the following steps.

1. Assemble the reactants out of the appropriate tiles.

2. Rearrange the reactants to form the products.

3. Figure out the number of each reactant and product required to make the equation balance. Write the numbers (the coefficients) in the boxes. If the coeffecient is 1, leave the box empty.

6 Challenge! Balancing difficult equations

Use the Periodic Table Tiles to help you balance these more complex equations.

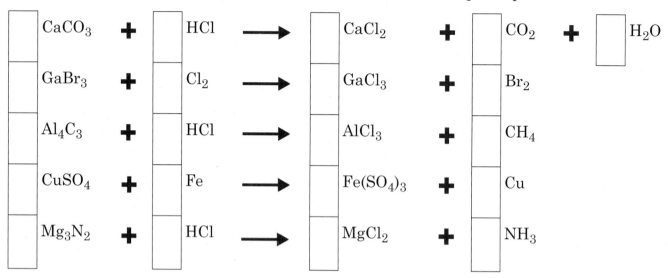

Each of these equations has three reactants.

Can you balance this equation without using the tiles?

$$\boxed{} \; C_{30}H_{62} \quad + \quad \boxed{} \; O_2 \quad \longrightarrow \quad \boxed{} \; CO_2 \quad + \quad \boxed{} \; H_2O$$

17B Conservation of Mass

How do scientists describe what happens in a chemical reaction?

A French chemist named Antoine Lavoisier was the first to prove the law of conservation of mass. This law states that the total mass of the reactants in a chemical reaction is always equal to the total mass of the products. This is not as easy to see as you might think! As you do this investigation, you will discover how tricky it is to show the law of conservation of mass.

Materials
- CPO Periodic Table Tiles
- Effervescent tablet
- Electronic scale (or triple-beam balance)
- Water
- Small paper cup

1 **Testing the reaction**

WARNING — This lab contains chemicals that may be harmful if misused. Read cautions on individual containers carefully. Not to be used by children except under adult supervision.

Step 1:
Tare the balance to zero with the empty cup.

Step 2:
Measure the mass of the water and the tablet.

Step 3:
Add the tablet to the water and observe the reaction.

Table 1: Conservation of mass data

Step	Data and observations
1. Find the mass of the effervescent tablet.	
2. Put the paper cup on the balance, and tare it to zero. Fill the cup about halfway with water. Record the mass.	
3. Put the tablet on the balance beside the cup, but don't put it in the water yet. Record the total starting mass.	
4. Drop the tablet into the cup of water. You can do this while the cup is still on the balance. Record your observations.	
5. Wait for the reaction to stop. Then, tap the cup gently to release as many bubbles as you can. Measure the mass.	
6. Subtract the final mass (5) from the starting mass (3). This is the mass difference between the products and reactants.	

2 Analyzing and interpreting data

a. Does this experiment agree with the law of conservation of mass? Using the data you just recorded, explain why or why not.

b. Explain why you observed a difference in mass. Where did the missing mass go? Did it really disappear?

3 Modeling the reaction

Scientists write chemical reactions like mathematical formulas. The reactants are to the left of the arrow, and the products are to the right of the arrow.

Use the tiles to model the chemical reaction.

Reactants → Products

The effervescent tablet contains a chemical called sodium bicarbonate. This chemical reacts with water according to the following reaction:

$$H_2O + NaHCO_3 \rightarrow NaOH + CO_2 + H_2O$$

1. Build the reactants side of the chemical reaction above ($H_2O + NaHCO_3$) using the Periodic Table Tiles.

2. Build the products side of the chemical reaction ($NaOH + CO_2 + H_2O$) using more Periodic Table Tiles.

4 Analyzing and interpreting data

Table 2: Counting atoms of each element

Element	Reactants	Products
Hydrogen		
Carbon		
Oxygen		
Sodium		

a. Fill in Table 2 with the numbers of each type of atom on the reactants side of the equation and on the products side of the equation.

b. How do the numbers of atoms of each element compare on each side of the equation? What does this imply for the law of conservation of mass?

c. In what phase is each reactant (solid, liquid, or gas)? In what phase is each product (solid, liquid, or gas)?

5 Proving that mass is conserved in a reaction

According to the law of conservation of mass, the mass of the products in a reaction is exactly equal to the mass of the reactants. Can you design an experiment to prove this is true for the reaction you observed in Part 1?

Examine the materials your teacher has given you. These include:

- Effervescent tablets
- 2 Beakers or flasks
- Water
- 2 Plastic pipettes
- 2 Self-sealing plastic bags
- Electronic scale or mass balance

1. Working with your lab partner, devise an experiment that will prove that mass is conserved in the reaction of the tablet and water. You may request additional materials if your teacher has them available.
2. List the materials you will need and how you will use them in the experiment.
3. List the steps you will follow in the experiment.
4. Before you begin, get approval for your procedure from your teacher.
5. If your experiment does not work, adjust your procedures and/or materials and try again.
6. Record your procedures, data, and results.

6 Communicating your results to the class

Prepare a brief presentation for the class about your investigation. Use the following format for your presentation.

a.	**Purpose**	What questions were you trying to answer?
b.	**Materials**	What materials and equipment did you choose and why?
c.	**Procedures**	What steps did you follow? You may demonstrate your procedures if time and materials allow.
d.	**Data**	What data did you collect?
e.	**Conclusions**	What does your data prove? If your experiment did not yield satisfactory results, what would you change in your procedures or materials. Why?

18A Energy and Chemical Changes

How do chemical changes involve energy?

Atoms come together to form compounds by making chemical bonds with other atoms. Chemical bonds are a form of energy. When atoms change bonds in a chemical reaction, energy can either be used or given off. In this investigation, you will make chemical reactions and deduce whether they use or give off energy.

Materials

- Temperature probe
- CPO DataCollector
- 5 g Sodium hydrogen carbonate (baking soda)
- Safety goggles
- Safety apron
- Electronic scale (or triple-beam balance)
- 100-mL Graduated cylinder
- 100 mL Vinegar
- 2 Foam cups
- 4-cm Piece of magnesium ribbon
- 50 mL Hydrochloric acid solution
- Paper towels

WARNING — This lab contains chemicals that may be harmful if misused. Read cautions on individual containers carefully. Not to be used by children except under adult supervision.

Special Safety Note: Use extreme caution when handling hydrochloric acid and other chemicals. Wear safety goggles and an apron during the entire investigation.

1 Making a prediction

What evidence should you look for that indicates a chemical change (a chemical reaction) is taking place?

2 Reaction 1: Magnesium and hydrochloric acid

In this reaction, you will observe the temperature while adding a 4-centimeter piece of magnesium ribbon to 50 milliliters of hydrochloric acid solution.

1. Measure 50 milliliters of hydrochloric acid solution, and place it in a pair of nested foam cups.
2. Place the temperature probe in the solution. Set the DataCollector to record one sample per second (default setting).
3. Measure a 4-centimeter piece of magnesium ribbon with a ruler.
4. When the temperature of the solution has stabilized, press start and drop the magnesium ribbon into the hydrochloric acid solution.
5. Stir the reaction continuously with the temperature probe.
6. Collect data until all the magnesium ribbon has disappeared and the temperature has stabilized.
7. Save the experiment and note the file name.

3 Constructing explanations

a. Study the temperature vs. time graph on the DataCollector. Did the temperature go up, go down, or stay the same during the experiment?

b. Why does a change in temperature indicate a change in energy?

4 Reaction 2: Vinegar and baking soda

In this reaction, you will add 5 grams of baking soda (sodium hydrogen carbonate) to 50 milliliters of vinegar (acetic acid solution).

1. Rinse the foam cup with water, then dry it with a paper towel.
2. Put 50 milliliters of vinegar in the pair of nested foam cups.
3. Place the temperature probe in the vinegar. Select a new experiment on the DataCollector, and make sure it is set to record one sample per second.
4. Measure 5 grams of baking soda with an electronic balance.
5. When the temperature of the vinegar has stabilized, press start and drop the baking soda into the vinegar.
6. Stir the reaction continuously with the temperature probe.
7. Collect data until the temperature stabilizes.
8. Save the experiment and note the file name.

5 Using your model

a. Study the temperature vs. time graph for the second experiment. Did the temperature go up, go down, or stay the same?

b. Look at the graph of each reaction. What is the maximum temperature change in each reaction? What does each graph show about energy changes in each reaction?

c. A reaction that gives off energy is called *exothermic*. Which reaction(s) are exothermic? Support your answer with your data.

d. A reaction that uses energy is called *endothermic*. Which reaction(s) are endothermic? Support your answer with your data.

6 Engineering and the design cycle   STEM

a. Use your knowledge of either exothermic or endothermic reactions to design a system that will keep a food item at a constant temperature.

b. Decide whether your system should keep a food item cold or hot.

c. Obtain more information for criteria and constraints for the design cycle from your teacher.

d. Areas for online research include food safety, insulation materials science, and thermal conductivity or energy transfer.

18B Thermodynamics of Hot/Cold Packs

Can we measure the heat released/energy absorbed by instant hot and cold packs?

All chemical reactions are either exothermic (release energy) or endothermic (absorb energy). However, some physical processes, such as dissolution (dissolving), can also release or absorb energy. This is the basis for commercially available instant hot packs and cold packs. Most hot and cold packs work by breaking a membrane that separates a solid and water. Once the membrane is broken, the solid dissolves in the water. Depending on the nature of the compound, heat is either released (hot pack) or absorbed (cold pack) during the process. In this investigation, you will examine the temperature changes of hot and cold packs and determine the energy absorbed or released during the chemical reactions that take place.

Materials

- 2 Foam cups
- Temperature probe
- CPO DataCollector
- Safety goggles
- Safety apron
- Water
- Calcium chloride (from an instant hot pack or ice melt)
- Ammonium nitrate (from an instant cold pack)
- Digital balance

WARNING — This lab contains chemicals that may be harmful if misused. Read cautions on individual containers carefully. Not to be used by children except under adult supervision.

1 Making predictions

Calcium chloride is used to melt ice on winter roads. Would that process be exothermic or endothermic? Why?

2 Doing the investigation

Part A: Hot pack—Record all measurements in Table 1.

1. Use a graduated cylinder to measure 50 milliliters of water. Record the mass of the water in Table 1. (*Hint*: 1 mL of water = 1 g)

2. Pour the water into two nested foam cups, then place the temperature probe into the water.

3. Use a balance to measure out about 10 grams of calcium chloride ($CaCl_2$). Record the mass of the $CaCl_2$ in Table 1.

4. Select new experiment on the DataCollector, and press go. Wait for the temperature of the water to stabilize, and record that temperature in Table 1 (initial temperature).

5. Pour the $CaCl_2$ into the water, and stir with the temperature probe.

6. Watch the graph and the temperature reading as the reaction proceeds.

7. Watch for the highest temperature reading before the temperature starts to go down again. Record that temperature in Table 1 (final temperature).

8. Pour the solution down the drain, then rinse and dry the foam cups.

Table 1: Hot pack mass and temperature data

Mass of water (g)	Mass of CaCl$_2$ (g)	Initial temp. (°C)	Final temp. (°C)

Part B: Cold pack—Record all measurements in Table 2.

1. Use a graduated cylinder to measure 50 milliliters of water. Record the mass of the water in Table 2. (*Hint*: 1 mL of water = 1 g)
2. Pour the water into two nested foam cups, then place the temperature probe into the water.
3. Use a balance to measure out about 10 grams of ammonium nitrate (NH_4NO_3). Record the mass of the NH_4NO_3 in Table 2.
4. Select new experiment on the DataCollector, and press go. Wait for the temperature of the water to stabilize, then record that temperature in Table 2 (initial temperature).
5. Pour the NH_4NO_3 into the water, and stir with the temperature probe.
6. Watch the graph and the temperature reading as the reaction proceeds.
7. Watch for the lowest temperature reading. Record that temperature in Table 2 (final temperature).
8. Pour the solution down the drain, then rinse and dry the foam cups.

Table 2: Cold pack mass and temperature data

Mass of water (g)	Mass of NH$_4$NO$_3$ (g)	Initial temp. (°C)	Final temp. (°C)

3 Arguing from evidence

a. Calculate the temperature change of the CaCl$_2$ and water reaction.

b. Calculate the heat gained by the solution using the equation below. Assume the specific heat of the solution is equal to the specific heat of water. The specific heat of water is 4.184 J/g°C.

> **HEAT EQUATION**
>
> $$E = mC_p (T_2 - T_1)$$

Where E = heat lost or gained
m = mass of solution
C_p = specific heat of substance
$T_2 - T_1$ = change in temperature (also referred to as ΔT)

c. Calculate the amount of energy (in joules) released per gram of $CaCl_2$. Remember, E is the opposite sign of the value you calculate.

d. Calculate the temperature change of the NH_4NO_3 reaction.

e. Calculate the heat lost by the solution using the heat equation in steb b. Assume the specific heat of the solution is equal to the specific heat of water.
Where E = heat lost or gained
m = mass of solution
C_p = specific heat of substance
$T_2 - T_1$ = change in temperature (also referred to as ΔT)

f. Calculate the amount of energy (in joules) absorbed per gram of NH_4NO_3. Remember, E is the opposite sign of the value you calculate.

4 Using your model

a. Look at the reactions below. Place the energy value on the appropriate side of the two equations.

$$CaCl_2(s) \rightarrow Ca^{2+}(aq) + 2Cl^-(aq)$$

$$NH_4NO_3(s) \rightarrow NH_4^+(aq) + NO_3^-(aq)$$

b. When $CaCl_2$ dissolves in water, the accepted value for $E = -747$ J/g. When NH_4NO_3 dissolves in water, the accepted value for $E = 326$ J/g. Compare your experiment values by calculating the percent error for each reaction. How well do your results agree with this published value?

c. Explain why your skin feels cool when a cold pack is applied, and why it feels warm when a hot pack is applied.

19A Solubility Curve of KNO$_3$

What is a solubility curve?

Solubility refers to the amount of solute that can be dissolved in a certain volume of solvent under certain conditions. In this investigation, you will be examining the relationship between temperature and the solubility of potassium nitrate (KNO$_3$). The solvent will be water. Using class data, you will construct a solubility curve for KNO$_3$.

WARNING — This lab contains chemicals that may be harmful if misused. Read cautions on individual containers carefully. Not to be used by children except under adult supervision.

Materials

- 5 Test tubes
- 400-mL Beaker
- Hot plate
- CPO DataCollector temperature probe
- Test tube holder (a spare 250-mL beaker works well)
- Potassium nitrate (KNO$_3$)
- 10-mL Graduated cylinder
- Water
- Electronic scale (or triple-beam balance)
- 400- or 600-mL Beaker
- Ice

1 **Making predictions**

Based on what you know about dissolving substances in water, do you predict that the solubility of KNO$_3$ will increase or decrease with temperature?

2 **Doing the investigation**

1. Fill a 400-milliliter beaker three-fourths full with water. Place the beaker on a hot plate. Allow it to heat while you go on to the next step.

2. Your teacher will assign you a specific amount of potassium nitrate (KNO$_3$). Use a balance to obtain the exact mass of KNO$_3$ you are assigned, and put it in a test tube. Record the mass in Table 1.

3. Add 5 milliliters of water to the test tube containing your KNO$_3$. Record this volume in Table 1.

4. Switch the DataCollector to meter mode. Place the test tube with the KNO$_3$ and water into your hot bath. Place the temperature probe into the test tube. Allow the solution to heat until all the KNO$_3$ dissolves, while stirring with the temperature probe. The solution temperature may need to reach approximately 85°C.

5. Once all solid has dissolved, remove the test tube from the hot water bath and allow it to cool. Leave the temperature probe in the test tube.

6. Watch for the first signs of crystallization in the test tube solution. (*Hint*: Stirring occasionally may help you see the small crystals that form.) When you start to see your first crystal gather at the bottom of the test tube, record the temperature in Table 1.

7. If crystals still do not form when the temperature has cooled down to 30°C, place the test tube in a beaker of room temperature water.

8. If the crystals still do not form when the temperature has cooled down to 25°C, take the test tube out of the room temperature water and place it in a beaker of ice water (provided by your teacher).

9. Show your teacher your results. If your teacher gives you permission, place your test tube back in the hot water bath, and redissolve the solid. Flush the solution down the drain with plenty of hot water.

10. Rinse, clean, and store all remaining apparatus.

Table I: KNO₃ crystal formation data

Mass of KNO₃ (g)	Volume of water (mL)	Mass of water (g)	Temp. when crystals first appeared (°C)

3 Calculations

a. In this investigation, you measured 5.0 milliliters of water. What is the mass of 5.0 milliliters of water? Explain.

b. Knowing how many grams of your solid can dissolve in 5.0 grams of water, how many grams could dissolve in 100.0 grams of water? Report this value to the class. (*Hint*: Set up a ratio.) Record your Part 2 results and those of the other groups in Table 2.

Table 2: Group Data

	Group 1 1 g	Group 2 2 g	Group 3 4 g	Group 4 6 g	Group 5 8 g
Temperature from Table I (°C)					
Solubility (g KNO₃/ 100 g H₂O)					

4 Using your model

a. Using the class data, construct a solubility curve. Plot the temperature (0°C–100°C) on the *x*-axis and the solubility of potassium nitrate (g KNO₃/100 g H₂O) on the *y*-axis. Make sure your graph has a title and that the axes are labeled, including units. When complete, connect all points with a smooth curve.

b. In your own words, explain how the solubility of KNO₃ varies with temperature.

c. From your solubility curve, predict the solubility of KNO₃ at

   1. 65°C
   2. 50°C
   3. 25°C

d. Is this solubility curve useful for temperature values above 100°C?

e. How many grams of KNO₃ can be dissolved in 200.0 milliliters of water at 35°C?

19B Acids, Bases, and pH

What is pH?

Life exists inside a certain range of pH values. A pH value describes whether a solution is acidic, basic (alkaline), or neutral by describing the concentration of hydronium ions in a solution. An acid is a substance that produces hydronium (H_3O^+) ions when dissolved in water, and a base (or alkali) is a substance that produces hydroxide (OH^-) ions when dissolved in water. Neutral solutions have equal numbers of H_3O^+ and OH^- ions. In this investigation, you will learn the pH of several common solutions by making a pH scale using a pH indicator and chemicals of known pH. You will then use your pH scale to identify two "mystery" solutions.

Materials (per group)

- 2 or 3 Well plates, depending on the size (need 12 wells)
- Permanent marker
- Eyedroppers or pipettes
- 5 mL Red cabbage juice (a pH indicator)
- 12 Red and 12 blue litmus papers (pH indicators)
- 2 mL each of 12 solutions
- 2 250-mL Beakers (1 containing warm water for rinsing pipettes; 1 empty for discarded rinse water)

WARNING — This lab contains chemicals that may be harmful if misused. Read cautions on individual containers carefully. Not to be used by children except under adult supervision.

1 Making predictions

Look at Table 1. Using the pH values listed, predict whether the antibacterial soap will be acidic or basic and whether the apple juice will be acidic or basic. Of the solutions in the list, to which are the soap and the juice most closely related?

2 Doing the investigation

A. Make a pH scale using indicators

1. To create your pH scale, you will use solutions 1 to 7 in Table 1. Place the following labels for these solutions in order on a well plate. If you don't have seven wells in a row on one well plate, place two plates side by side. The labels should describe the solution and its pH: Lemon – pH 2; Vinegar – pH 3; Seltzer water – pH 4; Red cabbage juice (the control) – pH 6.5; Baking soda solution – pH 8.5; Bar soap solution – pH 10; and Ammonia – pH 11.
2. Using a pipette, place 3 drops of red cabbage juice in each of the seven labeled wells.

3. Using a pipette, add 2 drops of each of the solutions to the appropriately labeled well. Use a different eyedropper or pipette for each solution. (If you must use the same dropper or pipette, thoroughly rinse it in fresh water after each solution.) Record the color changes in your data table. The color series you see on the plate(s) represents a pH scale. We will refer to it as the pH test plate. You will use it to identify the pH of other solutions.

4. Dip the red litmus paper and the blue litmus paper into each well of the pH test plate. Record the results according to the directions in the data table.

Table 1: pH Experiment data

Name of solution	Color when mixed with red cabbage juice	Red litmus paper: If paper turns blue, write "base" or make an "x."	Blue litmus paper: If paper turns red, write "acid" or make an "x."	pH
1. Lemon				2
2. Vinegar				3
3. Seltzer water				4
4. Red cabbage juice				6.5
5. Baking soda solution				8.5
6. Bar soap solution				10
7. Ammonia				11
8. Green tea				
9. Antibacterial soap				
10. Apple juice				
11. Mystery solution A				
12. Mystery solution B				

B. Using pH indicators to measure unknown pH

1. Repeat steps A2 through A4 for solutions 8 to 12. Use another well plate for these five solutions. The labels should describe the solution. At this point, you do not know the pH of these solutions.

2. Identify the pH of solutions 8 to 12. To do this, compare the color reactions and the litmus paper results for solutions 8 to 12 with the pH test plate.

3 Constructing explanations

a. What is the role of a pH indicator? What is the range of pH measured by each of the indicators you used (red cabbage juice, red litmus paper, blue litmus paper)?

b. Which of your solutions has the highest concentration of H_3O^+ ions? Which has the highest concentration of OH^- ions? Explain your reasoning.

c. The red cabbage juice used in the investigation has two roles. It is the pH indicator and, in the series on the pH test plate, it is a control. Why is a control needed on the pH test plate?

d. Mystery solutions A and B are identical to two other solutions you used in this lab. Use your results to identify these solutions. What is the identity of mystery solution A? What is the identity of mystery B? Support your claims with evidence.

e. List the pros and cons of using red cabbage juice and litmus paper as pH indicators.

f. There are various commercial and industrial uses for pH indicators, from developing photographs to maintaining swimming pool water. Find out how pH indicators work in these (or other) applications, and what the color changes mean.

20A Electricity

How do you measure voltage and current in electric circuits?

We use electricity every day, nearly every minute! In this investigation, you will build circuits and learn about voltage (volts) and current (amps), which are fundamental quantities that describe electricity.

Materials

- CPO Electric Circuits kit
- 1 D battery
- Multimeter with test leads
- Metal paper clip, plastic straw, piece of string, rubber band, pen cap, or other similar objects

1 Building a circuit

Single-bulb circuit

1. Build the circuit shown in the diagram with one battery, a switch, and a bulb.
2. Open and close the switch, and see what happens.

2 Constructing explanations

a. How can you tell electric current is flowing in the circuit? Can you see the current?

b. Current flows from positive to negative. Using your finger, trace the flow of current around the circuit.

c. How does the switch cause the current to stop flowing?

d. Why does the bulb go out when you open the switch?

3 Conductors and insulators

Materials through which electric current flows easily are called *conductors*.
Materials through which electric current does not flow easily are called *insulators*.

Connect circuit through each object.

Paper clip   Plastic straw

String   Rubber band

Pen cap

Close circuit here.

1.5 V

1. Break one connection in your single-bulb circuit.
2. Complete the circuit by touching different materials to the wire and the post to connect them.
3. Which materials allow the bulb to light (conductors)? Which do not (insulators)?

4 Constructing explanations

a. Make a table listing the materials as either conductors or insulators.

b. What characteristics are shared by the conductors?

c. What characteristics are shared by the insulators?

5 Circuit diagrams

We use the language of *circuit diagrams* to
describe electric circuits. In a circuit
diagram, wires are represented by solid
lines. Electrical devices like switches,
batteries, and bulbs are represented by
symbols.

a. Using these symbols, draw a diagram of
the circuit you built with one battery, a
switch, and a bulb.

Actual device   **Symbol**

Battery

Switch

Bulb

Wire

6 Measuring the voltage of a battery

Turn the dial of your multimeter to DC volts. Red goes to the positive terminal and black to the negative terminal. When you touch two points in a circuit with the leads, the meter reads the voltage between the points.

a. Measure the voltage of the battery, and record your reading.

b. Connect a second battery to the first by touching the ends together.

c. Measure and record the voltage for the four possible ways to connect two batteries (+ to –, + to +, – to –, – to +). How do these readings compare to the voltage of just one battery?

7 Measuring current

To measure current, the multimeter must be connected so that the current has to flow through it. This is different from voltage measurement. To measure current, you must force the current to flow through the meter by eliminating all other paths the current could go. Follow the instructions below carefully. Too much current can damage the meter.

1. Set the multimeter to measure DC amps (current).
2. Open the switch, and touch the red lead of the meter to the metal part of the switch closest to the battery's positive terminal (+).

3. Touch the black lead of the meter to the metal part on the other side of the switch.
4. The bulb should light, showing you that current is flowing through the meter. The meter displays the current in amps. This is the total current flowing through the circuit carrying power from the battery to the bulb. Remove the meter.

a. How much current is flowing through the circuit when the bulb is lit?

8 A circuit with a dimmer switch

The potentiometer (or pot) is an electrical device that can be used to make a dimmer switch. When the dial on the pot is turned one way, the pot acts like a closed switch, allowing current to flow freely. When the dial is turned the other way, the pot acts like an open switch, resisting the flow of current.

1. Connect the circuit in the diagram using the pot, a battery, wire, and a bulb.
2. Adjust the dial, and watch what happens to the bulb.
3. Use the meter to measure the voltage across the bulb for different settings of the pot. Record your data and observations in Table 1.

Table 1: Pot settings and voltage across bulb

Pot dial position	Voltage across bulb (V)	Observed light output of bulb

9 Constructing explanations

a. As you changed the settings of the pot, what happened to the voltage across the bulb?

b. Did you observe a relationship between the voltage across the bulb and the light output, or brightness?

c. Propose a relationship between power and voltage that would explain the light output of the bulb.

111

20B Resistance and Ohm's Law

What is the relationship between current and voltage in a circuit?

Electrical devices get the energy they use from the current that flows through them. When designing an electrical device or a circuit, it is important for the proper amount of current to flow given the available voltage. Resistance is the property of electricity that helps regulate the current in the circuit. You will explore resistance and Ohm's law, the equation that relates voltage, current, and resistance.

Materials

- CPO Electric Circuits kit
- 2 D batteries
- Multimeter with test leads

1 Mystery resistors

A *resistor* is used in a circuit to provide resistance. You have green, blue, and red resistors in your kit with values of 5, 10, and 20 ohms (Ω), but you don't know which is which!

1. Make a circuit with a switch, battery, and resistor, as pictured above.
2. Set the meter to measure current (DC amps). Open the switch. Measure the current by connecting the meter across the open terminals of the switch.
3. Set the meter to measure voltage (DC volts). Close the switch. Measure the voltage across the mystery resistor as pictured above.
4. Repeat the current and voltage measurements for each of the mystery resistors.

Table 1: Resistor currents

Resistor color	Voltage across resistor (V)	Current (A)

a. Use your knowledge of Ohm's law to determine which resistor is which. The resistance you calculate from Ohm's law will not come out exactly to 5, 10, or 20 ohms because the meter itself has a small resistance.

2 Resistance and potentiometers (pots)

The potentiometer (pot) you used in the previous investigation is really a *variable resistor*. A variable resistor allows you to change its resistance by turning a dial. Many dials you use every day, like dimmer switches, are actually potentiometers.

1. Use the meter to measure the resistance of the pot for different positions of the dial. The pot does not have to be in the circuit; you can just touch the leads across the pot.

2. Take your first reading with the pot turned all the way to the left. Then take four or five more readings until the pot is turned all the way to the right.

Table 2: Pot settings and resistance

Pot dial position	Resistance (Ω)

3 The bulb dimmer circuit

1. Build the dimmer circuit with two batteries, the pot, a switch, and a bulb.

2. Close the switch, then observe how the bulb brightness changes as you change the dial setting on the pot.

a. Use the concept of resistance to explain how the pot controls the brightness of a bulb.

4 The voltage drop

The voltage in a circuit is reduced whenever current flows through a device that has a resistance greater than zero. This reduction of voltage is called the *voltage drop*.

DC volts

To measure the voltage drop across the pot, touch the leads to (A) and (B).

Use points (B) and (C) to measure the voltage drop across the bulb.

Circuit diagram

1. Connect the dimmer circuit with the pot, a switch, two batteries, and a bulb.

2. The voltage drop is measured by touching the meter leads to the terminals of each device.

3. Measure the voltage drop across the pot and across the bulb for different dial settings of the pot. Record the observed light output at each dial position measured.

Table 3: Pot settings and voltage drops

Pot dial position	Voltage drop across pot (V)	Voltage drop across bulb (V)	Observed light output

a. What is the relationship between the voltage drop across the pot and the voltage drop across the bulb?

b. What does the voltage drop tell you about the electrical energy carried by the current?

c. What relationship do you observe between the measured voltage drops and the battery voltage?

21A Electric Circuits

What are the different types of circuits?

A simple electric circuit contains one electrical device, a battery, and a switch. Flashlights use this type of circuit. However, most electrical systems, such as a stereo, contain many electrical devices connected in multiple circuits. This investigation introduces two ways to connect multiple devices in a circuit.

Materials

- CPO Electric Circuits kit
- Multimeter with test leads
- 2 D batteries

1 Series circuits

Build this circuit.

1. Using two batteries, build the simple circuit with three light bulbs and a switch, as shown above.
2. Set the meter to DC volts. Close the switch, then measure the voltage across different places by touching the meter leads to the bulb terminals. Record the voltages in Table 1.

Table 1: Voltage measurements (V)

Between A and B (V)	Between B and C (V)	Between C and D (V)	Between A and D (V)

2 Constructing explanations

a. What relationships do you see among the voltage measurements in Table 1?

b. What do the voltage measurements tell you about the flow of energy in the circuit?

3 The current in series circuits

1. Set the meter to DC amps. Measure the current by opening the switch and touching the leads of the meter to the terminals of the switch in the three-bulb circuit. Record your measurements in Table 2.

2. Remove one bulb, and replace it with a wire. Measure and record the current for the two-bulb circuit.

3. Remove a second bulb, and replace it with a wire. Measure and record the current for the one-bulb circuit.

Table 2: Current measurements (A)

Three bulbs (A)	Two bulbs (A)	One bulb (A)

4 Constructing explanations

a. What happens to the current in the circuit as the number of bulbs is reduced? Explain why this occurs using Ohm's law and the concept of resistance.

b. What happens to the other two bulbs when one bulb is removed from the three-bulb circuit? Explain why.

5 Short circuits

A short circuit is an easy (but dangerous) shortcut for electric current that bypasses one or more of the electrical components in a circuit.

1. Rebuild your three-bulb circuit with the switch open.
2. Check the current, and observe which bulbs light and how bright they are.
3. Add a section of wire that bridges the last two bulbs in the circuit. This wire is the short circuit.
4. Complete the circuit (with the switch open), and use the meter to measure the current. Observe which bulbs light and how bright they are.

6 Constructing explanations

Table 3: Short circuit current measurements (A)

Three bulbs in series (A)	Three bulbs with two short circuited (A)

a. Compare the current in the three-bulb circuit with the current when two bulbs are bypassed by a short circuit. Which is greater? Use Ohm's law and the concept of resistance to explain why.

b. How does the current in the short circuit setup compare with the current you measured in a one-bulb circuit (see Table 2)? Explain why.

c. How does the resistance of a wire compare to the resistance of a bulb? Measure the resistances to test your answer. (*Note*: Most meters cannot measure very low resistance and display "0.00" when the resistance is lower than 0.01 ohms.)

d. Why would a short circuit be dangerous? Have a class discussion about the consequences of very large currents flowing through wires of different sizes.

7 Parallel circuits

Build this circuit.

1. Build a circuit with two batteries, a switch, and three bulbs, as shown in the diagram.
2. Close the switch, and measure the voltage across the battery. All three bulbs are lit.
3. Measure the voltage across each bulb by touching the leads of the meter to the terminals of each bulb separately.
4. Set the meter to DC amps. Measure the total current in the circuit by opening the switch and touching the leads of the meter to the terminals of the switch.

Table 4: Voltage and current in a parallel circuit

	Total circuit	Bulb 1	Bulb 2	Bulb 3
Voltage (V)				
Current (A)				

8 Constructing explanations

a. Compare the brightness of the bulbs in the parallel circuit with their brightness in the series circuit.

b. Compare the total current in the single-bulb circuit, the three-bulb series circuit, and the three-bulb parallel circuit. Propose a relationship among the currents that is supported by the brightness of the bulbs.

c. Do the other two bulbs remain lit when the third bulb is removed from the parallel circuit? Try it. How does this differ from what happened with the series circuit?

d. Do you think the electrical outlets in your home are connected in series or parallel circuits? Give two reasons why this type of circuit would be better for connecting outlets.

21B Electrical Energy and Power

How much energy is carried by electricity?

A voltage of one volt means one amp of current can do one joule of work in one second. This definition of a volt is really a formula for calculating power from current and voltage. If the voltage and current are multiplied, the result is the power used by the circuit. In this investigation, you will explore the relationship between voltage, current, and power.

Materials

- CPO Electric Circuits kit
- 1 D battery
- Multimeter with test leads
- Capacitor (Super Cap)
- CPO DataCollector

1 Energy and power in an electrical system

Electrical power

Voltage (V)

Power (W) $P = V I$

Current (A)

Voltage x Current = Power

$$\frac{watts}{amp} \times amp = watts (W)$$

Circuit diagram

A
Bulb
Switch
Battery
+ −

2. Connect a simple circuit with a single bulb, switch, and battery.
3. Use the multimeter to measure the voltage and current in the circuit when the bulb is lit.
4. Use the formula above to calculate the power used by the bulb in watts.
5. Repeat the experiment with two batteries connected so the bulb receives 3 volts instead of 1.5 volts.

Table 1: Power used by a bulb

Voltage (V)	Current (A)	Power (W)

2 Constructing explanations

a. How did the power used by the bulb compare at the two different voltages?

b. Was the bulb brighter, dimmer, or about the same at 3 volts compared to 1.5 volts? Explain any difference you observed using the concept of power.

3 Energy and power from a battery

Circuit diagram

Touch this wire here to charge the capacitor. Remove the wire after a few seconds.

Safety Note: The capacitor can be destroyed by connecting positive and negative voltage to the wrong terminals, or by using more than one 1.5 V battery.

Measure the voltage across the terminals of the capacitor.

1. Find the capacitor (labeled *super cap*). This capacitor acts like a battery that charges almost instantly when you touch its terminals to a battery.

2. Make the circuit in the diagram. The positive terminal of the capacitor should meet the red (+) lead of the meter. The meter will probably read 0 volts.

3. Touch the positive wire from the battery to the positive (+) terminal of the capacitor for 5 seconds. Remove the positive battery wire once the capacitor is charged to 1.5 volts.

4. Touch the leads of the multimeter across the capacitor, and watch what happens to the voltage (DC volts) over time. The bulb should light up, then dim and go out as the voltage drops.

4 Constructing explanations

a. How was energy flowing when the capacitor was charging? What was the source of the energy, and where did it go?

b. How was energy flowing when the bulb was connected and the battery was removed? What was the source of the energy, and where did it go?

c. Why did the bulb go out after a few seconds? Explain what you observed in terms of the ideas of energy and power.

5 Energy and power

In this part of the investigation, you will use the timer in stopwatch mode to measure how long the capacitor can keep one or more bulbs lit.

1. Set up the three circuits shown above, one at a time.

2. For each circuit, charge the capacitor for 5 seconds then use the DataCollector to measure how long the bulb produces light. Start the DataCollector when you close the switch to light the bulb. Stop the DataCollector when you can no longer see any light. Use stopwatch mode.

3. Repeat the test three times, and take the average. Use Table 2 to record your data.

Table 2: Energy and power data at 1.5 V

Starting voltage (V)	Number of bulbs	Time until bulb goes out (s)		Average of 3 trials (s)

6 Constructing explanations

a. What is the total power used by one, two, and three bulbs connected in parallel? In a parallel circuit, each device draws current as if it were the only device in the circuit. (*Hint*: Look back at your data from Part 1.)

b. What relationship do you observe between the time the bulbs stay lit and the total power used?

c. Since power = energy ÷ time, the formula can be rearranged to give energy = power × time. For example, if you use 10 watts for 10 seconds, you have used a total of 100 joules of energy (100 J = 10 W × 10 s.). Use your data to estimate how many joules of energy are stored in the capacitor at 1.5 volts.

22A Magnetism

How do magnets and compasses work?

Magnets are used in almost all electrical and electronic machines, from motors to computers. How far does magnetic force reach? How can you use a compass to detect magnetic forces? In this investigation, you will use magnets and a compass to answer these and other questions about magnetism.

Materials

- 2 Magnets (from kit)
- Compass (from kit)
- Metric ruler

1 How far does magnetic force reach?

How far does the magnetic force of a magnet reach? The answer is important, especially when dealing with machines that use magnets such as motors and generators .

How far does the magnetic force reach?

Record the distance at which the free magnet first moves.

Free magnet

0-cm mark

Test magnet

1. Place one magnet at the zero-centimeter mark of the ruler, and slide a second magnet closer and closer until the first magnet moves. Practice the technique several times before recording data.
2. Record the distance between the magnets when you first see movement.
3. Try each of the combinations of poles—north–north, south–south, and north–south.
4. For each combination, complete three trials, and average your three distances.

Table I: Magnetic forces between two magnets

	North–south	South–south	North–north
Distance 1 (mm)			
Distance 2 (mm)			
Distance 3 (mm)			
Average distance (mm)			
Average estimated error (mm)			

2 Analyzing and interpreting data

a. What is the average estimated error for each magnet combination? To find out, subtract each individual distance for the north–south magnet combination from the average of the three distances. Drop any negative signs. Once you have found these three differences, average them and record the value in Table 1. Repeat for the other two magnet combinations.

b. Are the attract and repel distances *significantly* different? Your answer should include a comparison between average estimated errors and the differences between magnet combination average distances.

3 Using a compass to detect magnetic forces

The needle of a compass is a permanent magnet. Earth is magnetic, so a compass needle is attracted to north in the absence of other (stronger) magnets.

Start:
Align the dial, arrow, and needle with north.

Measure the distance to deflect the needle 20 degrees East.

North pole — Magnet

Measure the distance to deflect the needle 20 degrees West.

South pole — Magnet

1. Set a compass on your table far from any magnets. Rotate the compass so the needle, dial, and arrow are all aligned with north.
2. Place a metric ruler beside the compass, and line it up perpendicular to the north pole of the compass. Move a small magnet along the ruler toward the compass, and note the distance at which the needle moves 20 degrees from north.
3. Reverse the pole of the small magnet and repeat. Note the distance at which the needle moves 20 degrees in the opposite direction.

4 Constructing explanations

a. At a distance of 10 centimeters, which is stronger: the magnetic force of Earth or the magnetic force of the small magnet? How is your answer supported by your observations?

b. Is the end of the compass needle a magnetic north or a magnetic south pole? How is your answer supported by your observations?

c. Is the geographic North Pole of Earth a magnetic north pole or a magnetic south pole? How is your answer supported by your observations?

123

22B Electromagnets

How are electricity and magnetism related?

Almost every electrical device that creates motion uses magnets. Permanent magnets are not the only type of magnets used in these devices. Often, electromagnets are used. Electromagnets create magnetic forces through electric currents. This investigation explores the properties of electromagnets.

Materials

- CPO Electric Circuits kit
- Electromagnet coil (in kit)
- Permanent magnet (in kit)
- Compass (in kit)
- 1 D battery

1 Electromagnets

1. Attach the coil, battery, and switch in the circuit shown above. Leave the switch open so no current flows.

2. Place a permanent magnet about one centimeter away from the coil. Stand the magnet up on its end.

3. Close the switch, and watch what happens to the magnet. *Don't* leave current running, or the coil will overheat. Open the switch after each trial.

4. Turn the permanent magnet around so its other pole faces the coil. Close the switch, and watch what happens now.

5. Reverse the wires connecting the battery to the circuit. This makes the electric current flow in the opposite direction. Repeat steps 3 and 4.

2 Constructing explanations

a. Write two to three sentences that describe what you observed when the switch was closed.

b. Propose an explanation for why the magnet moved.

c. When the magnet was reversed, how did the force between it and the coil change?

d. When the wires were reversed, did the force from the coil change direction? How do you know?

e. How is a current-carrying coil like a magnet? How is it different? Explain how this shows that electricity and magnetism are related.

3 Comparing the electromagnet to a permanent magnet

Permanent magnet

Adjust the distance of the permanent magnet so the compass needle is deflected 20 degrees away from north with the coil switched off (no current).

10 cm

Potentiometer

Coil

Compass

Switch

Battery

1. Attach the potentiometer, coil, battery, and switch in the circuit shown in the diagram. Leave the switch open so no current flows.

2. Set the compass so the needle, dial, and arrow are all aligned with north. Place the coil about 10 centimeters from the center of the compass.

3. Place a permanent magnet on the side of the compass opposite the coil. Bring the magnet close enough to deflect the needle 20 degrees away from north.

4. Close the switch and adjust the potentiometer so the needle returns to north. The coil should deflect the compass needle back toward north. Reverse the permanent magnet if the needle moves the wrong way. *Don't* leave current running, or the coil will overheat. Open the switch after each trial.

5. Try moving the permanent magnet to different distances and using the potentiometer to return the compass needle to north with force from the electromagnet.

4 Constructing explanations

a. The permanent magnet is pulling the compass needle to the left. The electromagnet is pulling the needle to the right. When the needle returns to north, what can you say about the magnetic forces from the permanent magnet and the electromagnet?

5 **Iron and electromagnets**

Trial 1: Coil only

Permanent
magnet

Measure the
current it takes
to bring the
compass needle
back to north.

Trial 2: Coil and steel pin

Permanent
magnet

1. Use the same circuit setup as in part 3 with one battery, switch, coil, and potentiometer.
2. Rotate the compass until the needle and dial are aligned with north. *There should be no magnets nearby and no current in the coil for this step.*
3. Move a permanent magnet close enough to deflect the needle 20 degrees from north.
4. The coil should be 10 centimeters from the center of the compass (see diagram above). Close the switch; then, use a multimeter to measure and record how much current it takes for the coil to bring the needle back to north. Adjust the current with the potentiometer. Once you have recorded the measurement in Table 1, open the switch to stop the current.
5. Put the steel pin in the coil so its head is against the coil and 10 centimeters from the center of the compass.
6. Adjust the distance of the permanent magnet so the compass needle is deflected 20 degrees from north, as you did in step 3. *There should be no current in the coil for this step.*
7. Close the switch; then, use a multimeter to measure and record the current it takes for the coil with the steel pin to return the needle to north.

Table 1: Electromagnet current with and without the steel pin

Current with bare coil	Current with steel pin	Difference in current	Percent difference

6 **Constructing explanations**

a. How did the steel pin affect the magnetic force created by the coil? Was the magnetic force reduced, increased, or unchanged? Use your observations to support your answer.

23A Harmonic Motion

How do we describe the back-and-forth motion of a pendulum?

Harmonic motion is motion that repeats in cycles. Many important systems in nature and many useful inventions rely on harmonic motion. For example, the phases of the Moon and cycle of the seasons are caused by Earth's harmonic motion. This investigation explores harmonic motion using a pendulum. You can apply the concepts you learn with the pendulum to other examples of harmonic motion.

Materials

- CPO DataCollector and 1 photogate
- CPO Physics Stand
- CPO Pendulum
- Graph paper

1 Setting up the pendulum

Attach the pendulum to one of the top holes in the stand.

Start the pendulum swinging, and watch it for a minute. Think about how to describe the motion.

a. Write one sentence about the motion of the pendulum using the word *cycle*.

b. The *amplitude* is the maximum amount the pendulum swings away from its resting position. The resting position is straight down. One way to measure amplitude is to measure the angle the pendulum moves away from center. Write one sentence describing the motion of the pendulum using the word *amplitude*.

c. Draw a sequence of sketches showing one complete cycle. Use arrows in each sketch to indicate the direction the pendulum is swinging at that point in the cycle.

2   Oscillators and period

a. Use the stopwatch mode of the DataCollector to measure the period of your pendulum. Time 10 cycles. Do three trials and record your data in Table 1.

b. Divide the average time for 10 cycles by 10 to get the period.

c. Write a one-sentence description of how you measured the period.

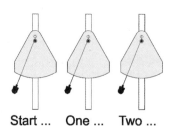

Count 10 cycles.

Start ...   One ...   Two ...

Divide time by 10.

example
period = 15.20 s ÷ 10
= 1.52 s

Table 1: Pendulum period data: Time for 10 cycles (s)

Trial 1	Trial 2	Trial 3	Average
Period of pendulum (average divided by 10)			

3   Measuring period with a photogate

Light beam

Knob

Photogate

Physics stand

Pendulum breaks light beam twice per cycle.

1. Attach the photogate as shown in the diagram. The pendulum breaks the light beam when it swings through the photogate. Try to keep the string length close to the length you used in Part 2, and try to release the pendulum bob straight so that it swings evenly through the photogate.

2. Put the DataCollector on the period function, and let the pendulum swing through the light beam.

3. A hold value can be displayed by pressing the memory (m) button on the lower right of the screen. The value is displayed to the right of the active value, which is always displayed.

4 Constructing explanations

a. Record the time measurement you get from the DataCollector.

b. Is the time you get from the DataCollector the period of the pendulum? Explain why or why not. (*Hint*: Compare to your results from Part 2.)

c. Explain how the time measured by the DataCollector is related to the period of the pendulum.

5 What variables affect the period of a pendulum?

In this investigation, the period of the pendulum is the only dependent variable. There are three independent variables: the mass of the bob, the amplitude of the swing, and the length of the string.

1. The amplitude can be changed by varying the angle that the pendulum swings.
2. The mass of the bob can be changed by adding or removing washers.
3. The length of the string can be changed by sliding it through the slot in the peg. Measure the length of the string from the bottom of the string peg to the bottom of the washers.

Design an experiment to determine which of the three variables has the greatest effect on the period of the pendulum. Your experiment should provide enough data to show that one of the three variables has a much greater effect than the other two. Be sure to use a consistent technique that gives you consistent results.

a. Design three experiments you can do to test how the variables affect the period. Summarize each experiment in one sentence.

b. Do the three experiments. Record your measurements in a data table.

6 Arguing from evidence

a. Of the three variables you can change (amplitude, mass, and string length), which one has the greatest effect on the pendulum period, and why? In your answer, be sure to consider how gravity accelerates objects of different mass.

b. Create separate graphs showing how each variable affects the period. To make comparisons easier, draw all the graphs with the same scale on the *y*-axis (period). The graphs should be labeled as in the example below.

7 Arguing from evidence

Pendulum clocks were once a common way to keep time. It is still possible to find beautifully made pendulum clocks today. To make a pendulum clock accurate, the period must be set so a certain number of periods equals a convenient measure of time. For example, you could design a clock with a pendulum that has a period of 1 second. The gears in the clock mechanism would then have to turn the second hand $1/60^{th}$ of a turn per swing of the pendulum.

a. Using your data, design and construct a pendulum that you can use to accurately measure a time interval of 30 seconds. Test your pendulum clock against the electronic stopwatch.

b. Mark on your graph the period you chose for your pendulum.

c. How many cycles did your pendulum complete in 30 seconds?

d. If mass does not affect the period, why is it important that the pendulum in a clock is heavy?

e. Calculate the percent error in your prediction of time from your pendulum clock. The percent error is 100 times the difference between your prediction and 30 seconds, divided by 30 seconds.

f. Suppose a watch manufacturer advertises that its quartz watch loses no more than 5 seconds per month. Assume that the watch loses the maximum amount (5 s) in 31 days. Calculate the percent error of the quartz watch by comparing 5 seconds to the number of seconds in a month.

Gears of clockworks

Pendulum

23B Natural Frequency and Resonance

What is resonance, and why is it important?

The pendulum oscillated at one frequency for each string length. The frequency at which an object vibrates is called its natural frequency. Almost everything has a natural frequency, and most things have more than one. We use natural frequency to create all kinds of waves, from microwaves to sound waves from guitar strings. In this investigation, you will explore the connection between the frequency of a wave and its wavelength.

Materials

- CPO DataCollector
- CPO Sound & Waves Machine
- Fiddlehead
- Wiggler
- CPO Physics Stand

⬛1 Setting up the investigation

Connect the DataCollector to the Sound & Waves console as shown in the diagram. The telephone cord connects the DataCollector and the Sound & Waves console. The stereo cord goes between the Sound & Waves console and the wiggler.

1. Attach the fiddlehead to the top of the stand, as high as it goes.

2. Attach the wiggler to the bottom of the stand, as low as it goes.

3. Stretch the elastic string a little (5–10 centimeters), and attach the free end to the fiddlehead. Loosen the knob until you can slide the string between any two of the washers. *Gently* tighten the knob just enough to hold the string.

4. Turn on the DataCollector, and plug in the AC adapter.

5. Set the Sound & Waves console to waves using the button. The wiggler should start to wiggle back and forth, shaking the string.

6. Set the DataCollector to timer mode in the frequency window. You should get a reading of about 10 Hz, which means the wiggler is oscillating back and forth 10 times per second.

7. Try adjusting the frequency of the wiggler with the frequency control on the Sound & Waves console. If you watch the string, you will find that interesting patterns form at certain frequencies.

DataCollector–CPO Timer mode
Choose "Frequency(*f*)" function.

2   Resonances of a vibrating string

At certain frequencies, the vibrating string will form wave patterns like those shown in the picture below. Each of the patterns occurs at a *resonance* of the string. The resonances, called harmonics, are described by the number of "bumps" seen on the vibrating string.

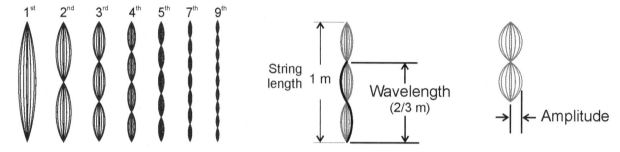

The wavelength of each harmonic is the length of one complete wave. One complete wave is two "bumps," so wavelength is the length of two bumps. Say a string is 1 meter long. If you have a pattern of three bumps, the wavelength is 2/3 meters, since three bumps equal 1 meter and one complete wave is two of the three bumps.

3   Finding the standing waves

You noticed that the standing waves only occur at certain special frequencies. The wiggler applies a periodic force to the string. When the periodic force matches the natural frequency of the string, a large response develops (resonance).

1. Use the frequency control to find the first through the eighth harmonics of the string (at least).

2. Record the frequency and wavelength for each harmonic in Table 1. You should fine-tune the frequency to get the largest amplitude wave before recording the data. Look for harmonics two to six before looking for the first harmonic. The first harmonic, also called the *fundamental*, is hard to find with exactness. Once you have the frequencies for the others, they provide a clue for finding the frequency of the first harmonic.

Table 1: Frequency, harmonic, and wavelength data

Harmonic #	Frequency (Hz)	Wavelength (m)	Frequency times wavelength
1			
2			
3			
4			
5			
6			
7			
8			

4 Constructing explanations

a. In one or two sentences, describe how the frequencies of the different harmonic patterns are related.

b. Why is the word *fundamental* an appropriate name for the first harmonic?

c. Write an equation relating frequency (f) and wavelength (λ) that best describes your observations.

d. If the frequency increases by a factor of 2, what happens to the wavelength?

e. Propose a meaning for the number you get by multiplying frequency and wavelength.

5 Frequency and energy

Waves are useful because they carry energy from one place to another. The energy of a wave can also carry information, such as a voice signal or a television picture.

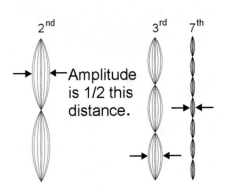

1. Set up several wave patterns, and measure the amplitude for each harmonic.

2. Measure at least five different harmonics, including the 6th or higher.

Table 2: Frequency vs. amplitude data

Harmonic #	Frequency (Hz)	Amplitude (cm)

6 Constructing explanations

a. What happens to the amplitude of the waves as their frequency increases?

b. How does the energy of a wave depend on its frequency if the amplitude stays constant? How is your answer supported by your observations of the vibrating string?

133

7 Resonance

The diagram below shows a useful way to think about pushing a swing. The person pushing applies a periodic force to the swing, just like the wiggler does to the vibrating string. Like the string, a swing is a system in harmonic motion. If the push is applied at the swing's natural frequency, the amplitude grows large, like the standing wave on the string. The response of a swing to a periodic push is an example of *resonance*. The harmonics on the vibrating string are another example of resonance. Resonance happens when the force applied to a system matches its natural frequency. We use resonance to create waves with specific frequencies, such as in a musical instrument, cell phone, or microwave oven.

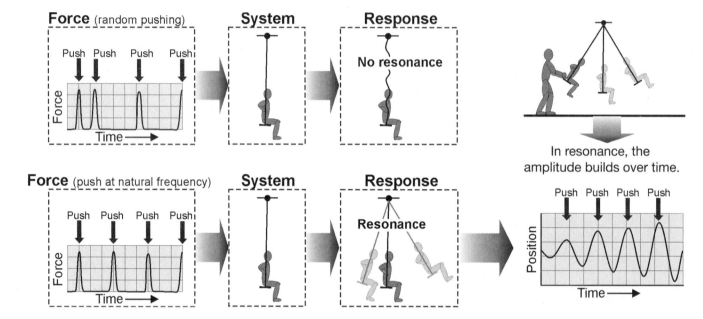

24A Properties of Sound

Do sound waves behave like other waves?

Sound is one of the most important of our senses. Sounds can express the whole range of human emotion. Scientifically, sound is one of the simplest and most common kinds of waves. Sound is a rich and beautiful palette from which musicians create works of beauty, excitement, and drama. In this investigation, you will listen to beats and explain if sound is a wave, create interference of sound waves, and demonstrate resonance.

Materials

- CPO DataCollector
- CPO Sound & Waves Machine
- Fiddlehead
- Wiggler
- Tuning forks

1 Beats, consonance, and dissonance

How do we know sound is a wave? What experimental evidence proves sound is a wave? Suppose two sounds reach your ear at the same time. Interference occurs when more than one wave is present at the same time, in the same place.

1. Your teacher will set up two sound waves generated by one machine operating in beat mode. One sound wave will be at 440 Hz, and the other will be at 445 Hz.
2. Listen to the 440 Hz sound by itself.
3. Listen to the 445 Hz sound by itself.
4. Listen to the combination of 440 Hz and 445 Hz together.
5. Now, your teacher will keep one sound at 445 Hz and adjust the frequency of the other one between 444 and 430 Hz. Listen to the combination.

2 Constructing explanations

The oscillations of loud and soft you hear from the two sound waves are called *beats*. Beats are caused by small differences in frequency between multiple sounds heard at the same time.

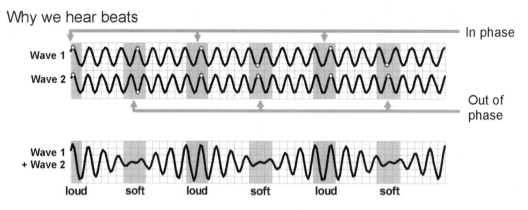

Why we hear beats

Conduct experiments that can answer the following questions about beats.

a. What makes the beats get faster or slower? In your answer, describe what you do to the frequencies to make the beats faster or slower.

b. Is the sound of beats pleasant to listen to or unpleasant? The word *consonant* is used by musicians to describe sounds that fit smoothly together. The opposite of consonant is *dissonant*. Dissonant sounds tend to make people anxious and irritable. Describe the relationship between consonance, dissonance, and beats.

c. How could you use beats to match one frequency to another frequency? This is done every day when musicians in an orchestra tune their instruments.

d. How different do two frequencies have to be before you do not hear any beats?

3 Interference

Beats are only one way sound waves interact. Suppose you have two identical sound waves and you are standing where you can hear them both. When you stand in certain positions, one sound wave reaches your ear in the opposite phase from the other wave, and the sound gets softer, like in beats. Move a little and the two sound waves add up to get louder. These effects, which are called interference, are easy to demonstrate.

1. Set up one sound generator with two speakers. Place one speaker about 0.5 meters behind the other.

2. Set the frequency between 400 Hz and 800 Hz.

3. Stand 3 or 4 meters in front of one speaker, and have your lab partner slowly move one of the two speakers away. You will hear the sound get loud, then soft, then loud again when the distance between the speakers has changed by one wavelength.

When two speakers are connected to the same sound generator, they produce identical sound waves. If you move around a room, you will hear places of loud and soft whenever your distance from each speaker differs by one wavelength.

4 Constructing explanations

a. Try to make an approximate measurement of the wavelength of sound by changing the distance between the two speakers. The speakers have been moved one wavelength when the sound heard by the observer has gone from loudest to softest and back to loudest again. For this to work, you need to keep the observer and both speakers in the same line.

b. Why do we not usually hear interference from stereos even though they have two speakers?

5 Resonance

Many objects that can create sound also demonstrate resonance. When struck, played, or rubbed, these objects produce a characteristic sound at their natural frequency. A tuning fork is a good example.

440 Hz Tuning fork

Sound generator   DataCollector

Frequency 440 Hz

1. Select a tuning fork, and tap it on your knee or another firm (but not hard) surface.

2. Listen to the sound. Does it change in frequency, or do you hear a single frequency that does not change?

3. Use the sound generator and DataCollector to measure the frequency of the resonance by matching the frequency of the sound generator with the sound you hear from the tuning fork. The match is perfect when you no longer hear any beats.

4. Try several different size tuning forks, and use the chart below to record the resonant frequency for each one.

Table 1: Resonant frequencies for tuning forks

Tuning fork description	Measured resonant frequency (Hz)	Labeled resonant frequency (if any)

6 Constructing explanations

a. Did you observe any relationship between the size (or shape) of the tuning fork and the frequency at which it was resonant?

b. What range of frequencies did you hear that seemed to match the frequency of the tuning fork? Give your answer in the form of a range, such as 429 Hz–451 Hz.

c. Strike the tuning fork and hold the bottom end against a hard, thin surface, like a window. Does the sound get louder, get softer, or remain unchanged? Explain what you hear by describing what might be happening between the tuning fork and the surface it is touching.

24B Resonance in Other Systems

How can resonance be controlled to make the sounds we want?

Almost all objects show some kind of resonance. A good example is a wine glass. If you rub a moistened finger around the rim of a wine glass, you can hear a resonant sound. Music is a combination of sound and rhythm that we find pleasant. Some people like music with a heavy beat and a strong rhythm. Other people prefer music that has notes that rise and fall in beautiful melodies. In this investigation, you will create musical notes by choosing frequencies of sound, make a simple musical instrument called a straw kazoo, and learn the foundations of musical harmony.

Materials

- CPO Sound & Waves Machine
- CPO DataCollector
- Wine glass
- Glass bottle
- Scissors
- Ruler
- Straw

1 Resonance in other systems

A. Wine glass

1. Obtain a good-quality wine glass, like the ones in the photo.

2. Hold the glass firmly at its base, and rub the rim with a moistened finger to hear the resonance.

3. Use the sound generator and DataCollector to match the frequency as close as you can to the sound of the glass.

4. Fill the glass to different heights with water, and use the same technique to find the resonant frequency for each different height.

Use different heights of liquid.

5. In Table 1, record the height of water and the resonant frequency you found for at least three trials.

Table 1: Resonant frequencies of glass of water

Trial #	Water height	Frequency (Hz)

B. Tall glass bottle

1. Use a tall glass bottle, like the ones in the diagram.

2. You can make a resonant sound by blowing over the open mouth of the bottle, as shown. This is a little tricky; you have to find the right angle for blowing air over the mouth of the bottle.

3. Fill the bottle to different heights of water, and see how the sound changes.

4. Use the sound generator and DataCollector to estimate the frequency of the sound you get at different heights, and record the results in Table 2.

Blow over the mouth of the bottle to make the sound.

Table 2: Resonant frequencies of bottle of water

Trial #	Water height	Frequency (Hz)

2 Constructing explanations

What was the relationship between the frequencies and the heights? In coming up with your answer, remember the waves on the vibrating string and how frequency and wavelength are related. Do you see similar behavior with the sounds and heights from the glass and bottle? For each case, what might be the vibrating element that would explain the changes in frequency?

3 Making notes

Musical notes are different frequencies of sound. Over thousands of years, people have found combinations of frequencies that sound good together. The frequencies are different enough to not make beats but not so different that they cannot make musical melodies.

1. Set up your sound generator and DataCollector.

2. Turn down the volume so you cannot hear the sound but can still read the frequency from the DataCollector.

3. Each group will be assigned a different frequency to tune to. Tune your frequency using the DataCollector until you are within 1 Hz of your group's frequency.

Your teacher will tell you to adjust the volume of different frequencies so they can be heard together. Don't change the frequency; just turn the volume up or down when you are told.

a. Describe the sound of the three frequencies—264 Hz, 330 Hz, and 396 Hz—when you hear them together. Which three notes are these? (Look at the diagram below.)

b. Describe the sound of the three frequencies—264 Hz, 315 Hz, and 396 Hz—when you hear them together.

c. Contrast the two sounds. Does one sound more happy or sad than the other? Does one sound spookier than the other? Which combination reminds you more of spring? Which reminds you more of fall?

d. Describe the effect of adding a frequency of 528 Hz to each combination of frequencies.

C major Scale								
Note	C	D	E	F	G	A	B	C
Frequency (Hz)	264	297	330	352	396	440	495	528
Ratio to C-264	$\frac{1}{1}$ $\left(\frac{264}{264}\right)$	$\frac{9}{8}$ $\left(\frac{297}{264}\right)$	$\frac{5}{4}$ $\left(\frac{330}{264}\right)$	$\frac{4}{3}$ $\left(\frac{352}{264}\right)$	$\frac{3}{2}$ $\left(\frac{396}{264}\right)$	$\frac{5}{3}$ $\left(\frac{440}{264}\right)$	$\frac{15}{8}$ $\left(\frac{495}{264}\right)$	$\frac{2}{1}$ $\left(\frac{528}{264}\right)$

4 Controlling frequency and wavelength

Most musical instruments use resonance. This means that when instruments are played, the sounds they make are based on their natural frequencies. How do musical instruments make so many notes at different frequencies? Why does a guitar player use frets while a flute player uses different fingerings?

These musicians are controlling the frequencies of their instruments by changing the wavelength of the vibrating string or column of air. If the wavelength is shorter, the frequency goes up. If the wavelength is longer, the frequency goes down. The chart on the previous page shows the ratios of frequency to make a musical scale. If the frequency goes up, the wavelength must go down proportionally. That means to double the frequency, the wavelength is reduced by half. To make the frequency 3/2 higher (to get the note E), the wavelength must be 2/3 because $2/3 \times 3/2 = 1$.

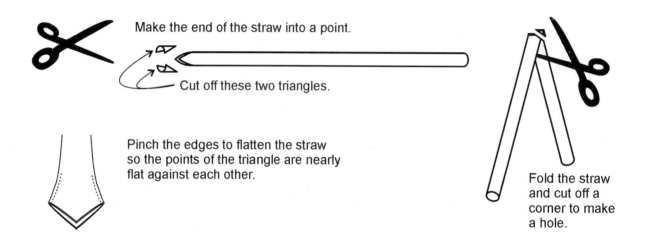

Make the end of the straw into a point.

Cut off these two triangles.

Pinch the edges to flatten the straw so the points of the triangle are nearly flat against each other.

Fold the straw and cut off a corner to make a hole.

a. Make a straw kazoo, and blow through it to make some sound. Cut off the blunt end of the kazoo. What happens to the frequency of the sound it makes?

b. Fold the straw, and cut a small hole exactly in the middle of your kazoo. Cover the hole with your finger. While blowing through the kazoo, lift your finger to cover and uncover the hole. What happens to the sound? (*Hint*: The vibrating object in the straw is a column of air.)

c. Identify at least three musical instruments that produce sounds using vibrating objects of different lengths. For each instrument, explain how the length of the vibrating object is changed to make music.

25A Color

What happens when you mix different colors of light?

All the colors of visible light can be created artificially using a combination of three primary colors: red, blue, and green. In this investigation, you will use a white light source and color filters to discover what happens when you mix different colors of light. You will also learn how the filters work.

Materials
- CPO Optics with Light & Color kit
- Colored pencils

1 Sources of light

a. Compare the light from a light bulb with the light from the same bulb when seen in a mirror. In both cases, describe the path of the light from the source to your eyes.

b. Look at your clothes. Does the light reaching your eye from your clothes originate in your clothes or somewhere else?

c. Turn off all the lights, and shade the windows so it is completely dark. Can you see your clothes in the dark? What does this experiment tell you about whether your clothes give off their own light or reflect light from somewhere else?

d. Turn on a television or computer screen in a dark room. Can you see the TV or computer screen in the dark? What does this experiment tell you about whether the TV or computer screen gives off its own light or reflects light from somewhere else?

2 Making colors

1. Slide all three flashlights into their own light holders.
2. Connect the red and green flashlights by sliding their holders together using the rail and slot connectors on the side.

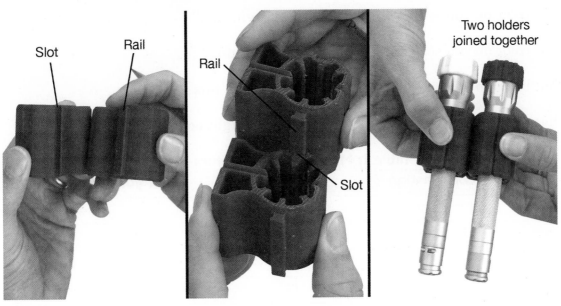

3. Place the blue flashlight on top of the red and green lights, making a small pyramid stack. Position the blue light on its side so the rail on the holder fits in the small groove between the red and green light holders. Turn the three lights on.

Flap provides shade to see color mixing better.

Fold flap over.

Colored lights

Slotted side facing up

Box

Light blue lens

Colored lights shine here.

4. Set the light blue lens, slotted side up, just in front of the lights so they shine through it.

5. Set the white box that the Optics with Light & Color kit comes in on the opposite side of the paper from the lights. Fold the top flap of the box over to shade the area where the three colored lights are shining on the box.

6. Slowly move the lens away from the lights and toward the box until you see the three spots of color (red-green-blue) overlap on the "screen."

Rail on blue light holder

Groove between red and green lights

3 Constructing explanations

a. What color do you see where red and green light mix?

b. What color do you see where red and blue light mix?

c. What color do you see where blue and green light mix?

d. What color do you see where all three colors of light equally mix?

Table 1: Mixing primary colors of light

Color combination	Color you see
Red + Green	
Red + Blue	
Blue + Green	
Red + Green + Blue	

e. Research and explain the following terms from the diagram below: cone cells, rod cells, retina.

f. Research and explain how the eye sees white light in terms of the photoreceptors in the eye.

Photoreceptors in the eye

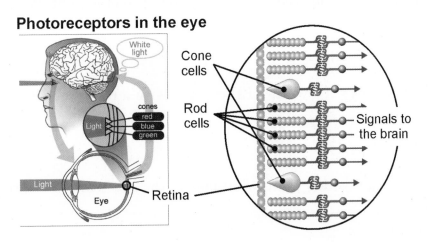

4 How does a color filter work?

A red laser can produce a single pure color of red, which can be useful in some applications. For example, making three-dimensional images, called holograms, requires a pure source of light, which a laser can provide.

The Optics with Light & Color kit includes three different sources of colored light, but just how "pure" are these colors? In this part of the investigation, you will examine the light produced by each colored light and learn how a color filter works. Use the diffraction glasses to make your observations.

1. Examine the red light with the diffraction glasses.
2. Using colored pencils, sketch what you see in the appropriate column of Table 2.
3. Repeat steps 1 and 2 for the green and blue lights.
4. Remove one of the color filters from one of the colored lights. Examine the light produced by the white LED, and record your observations in the table.

Table 2: Examining colors

Red light	Green light	Blue light
White light		

5 Arguing from evidence

a. Compare the colors in the red light to those in the green light. What are the similarities and differences in the range of colors?

b. Compare the colors in the green light to those in the blue light. What are the similarities and differences in the range of colors?

c. How do the colors in the white light compare to the red, green, and blue lights combined?

d. The red light consists of a white LED covered with a red filter. What does the red filter do?

e. What do color filters do?

f. If you wanted to get yellow light, what part of the spectrum would the color filter have to absorb?

25B Reflection and Refraction

How does light behave when its path is changed?

When we look in a mirror, we see a twin of ourselves reversed left to right. A fish underwater appears to be in a different place from where it really is. Both of these illusions are caused by the bending of light rays. This investigation explores reflection and refraction, two processes that bend light rays. You will also use refraction to calculate the focal point of a lens.

Materials

- CPO Optics with Light & Color kit
- Protractor and metric ruler
- Index card
- Pencil
- 2 Sheets of graph paper
- Sheet of blank white paper

1 Observing the law of reflection

How to trace the beam of the laser

Find the laser spot on edge of index card.

Laser spot

Follow the edge down to the graph paper.

Make a mark on the paper directly below the spot on the edge of the index card.

1. Set a sheet of graph paper on your lab table.
2. Slide the laser into a holder, turn the laser on, and put it on the graph paper.
3. Align the laser so the beam follows one horizontal grid line across the graph paper.
4. To line up the beam with the line on the graph paper, place an index card on its side on the paper. Keeping its long edge flat on the graph paper, slowly slide the card until you can just start to see the beam on the short edge of the card. Follow this edge of the index card down, and make a mark on the paper. The mark tells you where the beam is. You can use this method to trace the path of the beam in all the Optics with Light & Color activities.
5. Follow the beam as it shines across the graph paper, and make sure it lines up with one of the horizontal lines on the paper.
6. Set the mirror long side down on the graph paper, so the light beam from the laser hits its shiny front at an angle.
7. Draw a line on the graph paper marking the position of the front face of the mirror.

Beam reflecting off mirror

Tracing reflected beam with index card

Laser horizontally aligned

147

8. Use a pencil and the index card to trace the light ray going toward and away from the mirror. Label it ray 1.

9. Draw small arrows every couple of inches indicating the direction the beam is traveling.

2 Constructing explanations

Drawing the ray diagram

a. A diagram showing how light rays travel is called a *ray diagram*. Lines and arrows on a ray diagram represent rays of light.

b. Look at your ray diagram showing the surface of the mirror and ray 1 before and after hitting the mirror.

c. Which is the incident ray? Label it on your ray diagram.

d. Which is the reflected ray? Label it on your ray diagram.

3 The law of reflection

a. Move the laser and the mirror to a new location on the graph paper. Make sure the beam hits the mirror at a slightly different angle, and repeat steps 7–10. Be sure to label each ray. Continue shining and tracing the beam from a total of four locations. Label the rays 1–4.

b. For each ray diagram, draw a line perpendicular to the mirror surface at the point where the ray hits. This line is called the *normal line*.

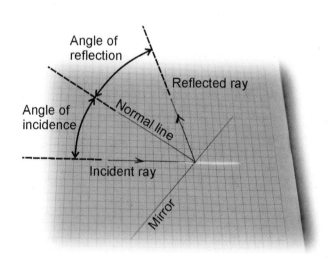

c. Use a protractor to measure the angle between the normal and the incident and reflected rays. Record your measurements in Table 1.

d. Write your own statement of the law of reflection, describing the relationship between the angles you measured.

e. A laser shines at a mirror at an angle of incidence of 75 degrees. Predict its angle of reflection. After predicting, test your prediction. Were you right?

Table 1: Angles of incidence and reflection

	Diagram 1	Diagram 2	Diagram 3	Diagram 4
Angle of incidence				
Angle of reflection				

4 Light rays going through a prism

A prism is a solid piece of clear glass or plastic with polished surfaces. Prisms are useful for investigating how light bends when it passes from one material into another, such as from air into glass or glass into air.

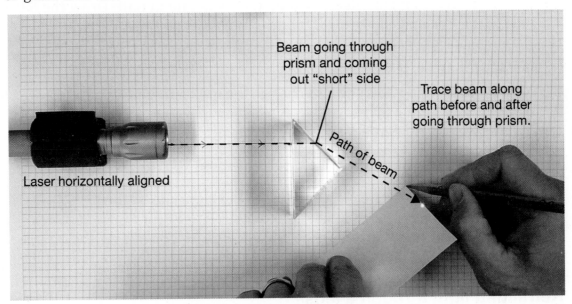

1. Flip your graph paper over, and set the laser on the left side of the paper. Turn the laser on, and face it so it is shining horizontally across the paper.
2. Place the prism in the middle of the paper in the laser beam, so the beam comes out the opposite short side.
3. Rotate the prism in the beam, and observe where the beam comes out.
4. Keep rotating the prism until you can see the beam refracted and reflected at the same time.

5 Sketching what you observed

a. Draw at least one ray diagram showing a laser beam that is refracted. The *refracted ray* is the ray that passes through the prism and comes out at a different angle.

b. Draw a ray diagram showing a laser beam that is reflected.

c. Draw a ray diagram showing a laser beam that is both refracted and reflected.

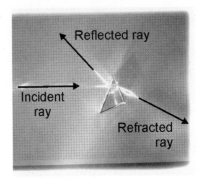

149

6 | Seeing reflection and refraction at the same time

Both refraction and reflection often occur when light hits a boundary between materials, such as the boundary between glass and air. The amount of light reflected or refracted depends on your viewing angle relative to the surface.

Fold a paper card marked with A and B.

The image in the prism changes as you move your head!

1. Take a piece of graph paper about the size of a business card, and draw a line about 5 centimeters from one edge, dividing the rectangle in half. Draw the letter A on one side of the line and the letter B on the other side, as shown above.

2. Fold the paper on the line, and wrap it around one of the edges of the prism that is not a right angle.

3. Move your head up and down to change the angle at which you look into the prism.

7 | Constructing explanations

a. Draw a diagram showing the path of the light when you see the letter A.

b. Draw a diagram showing the path of the light when you see the letter B.

c. Is the image in the prism always reflected or refracted, or can reflection and refraction occur at the same time?

8 | Refracting light through a lens

1. Divide a new sheet of graph paper in half horizontally. For the first part of this activity, use the top half of the new sheet of graph paper. Place the laser on the edge of the paper, and shine the laser so it follows a horizontal grid line across the paper.

2. Place the light blue lens 10 centimeters to the right of the laser with the slot facing up. Line the lens up vertically using the grid lines on the graph paper. It is important that the beam is perpendicular to the lens. Make sure the beam of the laser is lined up with the middle of the lens. Lines on the side of each lens indicate the middle.

3. Trace around the base of the lens so you can remove it and put it back to complete ray tracing.

4. Shine the laser through the lens so the beam passes off-center, almost at the very outer edge of the lens. Set the block with the mirror about 30 centimeters to the right of the lens so the beam hits it after passing through the lens. Use the side of the block with the graph paper on it so you can clearly see where the beam hits the block.

5. Trace the laser beam before and after it passes through the lens. Be sure to mark the points where the beam exits the laser, enters the lens, exits the lens, and then hits the block. Connect all these points to see the path of the beam.

6. Realign the laser with a different horizontal grid line parallel to the original beam and closer to the center of the lens. Again, trace the path of the beam before and after it passes through the lens.

7. Realign the beam so it passes directly through the center, and trace the beam again.

8. Trace two more beams passing through the lens on the other side of the center of the lens for a total of five beams. Label the beams 1–5 on both sides of the lens.

9. Repeat steps 1–8 with the dark blue lens using the bottom half of the graph paper.

9 Constructing explanations

a. Feel the glass surface of each lens with your fingers. Note the shapes of the lenses. How are the lenses different?

b. Sketch the shape of each lens (without the stand) from the side. Label each lens.

c. Describe the paths of the rays before and after they passed through the light blue lens. Include the words *refract*, *converge*, and *diverge*.

d. What is the focal point of a lens? Mark the focal point on the first ray diagram.

e. What is the focal length of the lens? Measure the focal length of the light blue lens.

f. Describe the paths of the rays before and after they passed through the dark blue lens. Include the words *refract*, *converge*, and *diverge*.

g. How are the two lenses different?

h. One lens is referred to as a diverging lens, the other as a converging lens. They are also sometimes referred to as convex or concave. Research these terms, and explain which lens is which.

10 Making an image with a lens

Certain types of lenses can make an image of a distant light source. The image forms about one focal length away from the lens when the object is far away.

1. Find a wall at least 5 meters from a light source or sunlit window. Tape a piece of white paper to the wall to create a screen for seeing the image.

2. Hold the light blue lens at different distances parallel to your screen and light source or window. Try distances between 15 and 25 centimeters from the screen.

3. Move the lens until you see a sharp image of the light source or window on the screen. An image is produced when your lens is about one focal length from the screen.

4. Measure the distance from the lens to the screen, and record the focal length in Table 2. Repeat the procedure with the dark blue lens.

Table 2: Focal lengths of lenses

	Focal length (cm)
Light blue Lens	
Dark blue lens	

Images of objets can be smaller or larger than the objects themselves. Images can also be right side up or inverted.

a. Was the image created by the light blue lens smaller or larger than the object?

b. Was the image right side up or inverted?

11 Projecting an image with a lens

You can think about a lens as collecting a cone of light from each point on an object. For a perfect lens all the light in the cone is bent so it comes together at a point again to make the image. This is how movie projectors project an image on film onto a screen.

Slowly move the lens toward the light until a sharply focused image appears on the wall or screen.

Light projected onto wall or screen at least 5 meters away

1. Place one of the lights near the edge of the graph paper. Put the F filter on the light, and shine it horizontally.

2. Set the light blue lens on the graph paper 35 centimeters from the light.

3. Shine the light at a distant light-colored wall at least 5 meters away. If one is not available, tape a piece of paper to the wall as your projection screen. Slowly move the lens toward the light until you see a sharp image of the F on the wall or screen. Have one group member check the projected image closely while the lens is slowly moved to find the exact lens position where the F comes into focus.

   At what distance from the light does the lens produce a sharp image?

4. Use a paper card to block some of the light from the lens. The card should be 2 to 3 centimeters from the lens and on the same side as the light.

Observe the image on the wall or screen as you slowly cover and uncover the lens.

12 Constructing explanations

a. Describe the characteristics of the image formed by the lens. Characteristics include whether the image is right side up or inverted, and whether it is larger or smaller.

b. Discuss with your class why blocking part of the lens makes the image dimmer, even though you still see the entire image.

c. *Challenge*: The thin lens formula is used to calculate the exact focal length of a lens. Calculate the focal length of your light blue lens using the thin lens formula. The distance of the object from the lens is 35 centimeters. You will need to measure the distance from the lens to the sharply focused image. How does this focal length compare with the other two focal lengths of the light blue lens you measured? Was the method from Part 8 or Part 10 more accurate compared to the focal length calculated using the thin lens formula?

The thin lens formula

f = focal length of lens

d_i = distance of image from lens

d_o = distance of object from lens

$$\frac{1}{f} = \frac{1}{d_i} + \frac{1}{d_o}$$

Optional Investigations

The investigations in this section are designated as C Level. They are not required as part of the course but may be used to further explore and extend the concepts in the chapter.

1C Significant Digits

How do we make precise measurements?

We often need to measure distances in everyday life, whether to find the height of a person, the length of a rug, or the width of a doorway. In this investigation, you will learn how to make precise measurements and how to record them using the correct number of significant digits.

Materials

- Meter stick
- Small ruler
- Pencil
- Paper clip
- 2 Thick books

1 Significant digits and measuring length

Science and engineering require precise measurements. A measurement that is a millimeter off could cause serious problems if you are designing parts for a computer, a car engine, or a satellite. Measuring carefully is important if you wish to be precise, but having the right tool for the job is also key. Suppose you want to measure the mass of a quarter. Would you use a bathroom scale designed to weigh people or a small digital scale?

When recording a measurement, you are only allowed to record the meaningful, or significant digits.

Significant digits are those that you are certain of plus one additional estimated digit.

Consider the length measurement shown to the right. The pencil looks to be a little more than 7.5 centimeters long. Should the length be recorded as 7 centimeters? 7.5 centimeters? 7.9 centimeters? 7.90 centimeters?

When the tip of the pencil is lined up with the 0-centimeter mark, you can definitely tell that the pencil is between 7.9 centimeters and 8.0 centimeters. You can therefore be sure of the 7 and 9 in your measurement; these are significant digits.

You can make the measurement more precise by estimating one more digit. The end of the pencil eraser may look like it's on the 7.9-centimeter mark or right on the 8.0-centimeter mark, so the length falls between 7.90 and 8.00 centimeters. You might estimate the length to be 7.95 centimeters. It's impossible to pinpoint the last digit exactly, and someone else might record the length as 7.90 centimeters. However, you could *not* record the length as 7.950 centimeters because both the five and the zero would be estimated.

2 Making measurements

Use either a meter stick or a small ruler to make the following measurements in centimeters using the correct number of significant digits.

a.   The length of a sharpened pencil

b.   The diameter of a pencil eraser

c. The length of a paper clip

d. The height of your desk or table

e. The length of your classroom

3 Arguing from evidence

a. For which measurements did you use the meter stick? Why?

b. Which measurement was the most precise?

c. Which measurement was the least precise?

d. Describe two ways you could have made more precise measurements. You may include using tools other than the ruler and the meter stick.

e. The distances you measured were relatively small. How could you measure a longer distance, such as the length of the schoolyard or the distance from your school to your house?

4 Another way to measure

Sometimes it is possible to use the tools we have in a creative way to make measurements more precise. You will need two different thick books such as textbooks or reference books.

a. Suppose you want to measure the thickness of a single page in each of the books. Can you do this with a ruler? Try it, and record your measurements using the correct number of significant digits.

b. According to your measurements, are the thicknesses significantly different?

c. Discuss with your group a better way to measure the thickness of one page. Describe the steps you follow to make your measurements. Record your data, and show any calculations. Use the correct number of significant digits to express your answers.

d. How many significant digits do your thickness measurements have now? How does this compare to the number of significant digits in your measurements from step a?

e. According to your new measurements, are the thicknesses significantly different?

f. Describe another measurement you could make using a method similar to the one you used in step c.

2C Thickness of Aluminum Foil

What is the thickness of aluminum foil?

In this investigation, your challenge is to determine the thickness of aluminum foil. Foil is obviously much too thin to measure with a ruler, so how will you meet the challenge? You will use your knowledge of density, volume, and area to arrive at a value and compare it to the findings of your classmates.

Materials

- Aluminum cylinder
- Aluminum foil
- Electronic scale (or triple-beam balance)
- Ruler
- 50-mL Graduated cylinder
- Scissors
- Water

1 Doing the investigation

1. Obtain an aluminum cylinder from your teacher, and measure and record its mass in Table 1.

2. Measure 20 milliliters of water in the graduated cylinder, and record the volume in Table 1.

3. Carefully place the aluminum cylinder in the graduated cylinder, and record the combined volume in Table 1.

4. Cut out a 20-centimeter-by-20-centimeter piece of aluminum foil, and measure and record its mass in Table 1.

2 Analyzing and interpreting data

Is the density of the aluminum cylinder and the aluminum foil the same?

Table 1: Aluminum data

Mass of aluminum cylinder (g)	Volume of water (mL)	Volume of water and aluminum (mL)	Mass of aluminum foil (g)	Dimensions of aluminum foil (cm x cm)

3 Arguing from evidence

a. What is the volume of the aluminum cylinder as calculated by water displacement?

b. What is the density of the aluminum cylinder? (Remember, density equals mass divided by volume, or $D = m/V$.)

c. Using the density of the aluminum cylinder and the mass of the aluminum foil, calculate the volume of the foil in milliliters.

d. What is the volume of foil in cubic centimeters (1 mL = 1cm^3)?

157

e. What is the area of the aluminum foil in square centimeters?

f. Calculate the thickness of the aluminum foil by dividing the volume by the area.

4 Constructing explanations

a. How does your answer compare with your classmates' answers?

b. Research aluminum foil. Is it pure aluminum? Be sure to cite your sources.

c. Do you think it is reasonable to use the density of the aluminum cylinder for your aluminum foil calculation?

d. A very thin layer of gold plating was applied to a metal tray measuring 25.22 centimeters by 13.22 centimeters. The gold plating increased the mass of the tray by 0.0512 grams. Find the thickness of the plating. The density of gold is 19.3 grams per cubic centimeter.

3C Looking for Significant Differences

Do you really need photogates to study the motion of the Energy Car, or is a stopwatch good enough?

People often ask if electronic timing is really necessary when conducting classroom motion experiments. Isn't a stopwatch good enough? To explore this question, you will compare travel times for the Energy Car with and without a homemade "sail." You will collect time data with photogates and with a simple stopwatch. Keep in mind that *significant differences* are differences that are much larger than the estimated uncertainty (or error) in the results. That means two results are "the same" *unless* their difference is much greater than the estimated error.

Materials

- CPO DataCollector and 2 photogates
- CPO Energy Car and Track
- CPO Physics Stand
- Steel marble
- Tongue depressor
- Large paper plate
- Tape

1 Making a prediction

You will compare travel times for the Energy Car as it rolls down a gentle slope with and without a paper plate sail. You will collect travel times using photogates and a stopwatch.

a. Write your hypothesis for how the sail will affect the travel time of the car.

b. Write your hypothesis for how the photogate times will compare to the stopwatch times for the same types of trials.

2 Setting up the investigation

Attach track to first hole from bottom.

A goes here.

1 marble in car

B goes here.

Adjust the plunger so the car tab almost breaks the beam, but not quite.

1. Assemble a straight track, and attach it to the first hole from the bottom of the stand.
2. Place one stop at the top of the track and one at the bottom. Place a lump of clay on the plunger at the bottom of the track so the car won't bounce back through the photogate.
3. Attach the photogates as shown. Put photogate A at the top of the track.

4. Put one steel marble in the center of the Energy Car.

5. Place the Energy Car at the top of the track so it rests against the stop's plunger. Adjust the plunger so the light beam is just about to be broken by the tab sticking straight up on the car. (As you change the plunger position, the tab on the car will move in and out of the beam.) Watch the photogate's green/red light indicator. The light should be green but about to become red as soon as you release the car.

3 Doing the investigation

1. Roll the car down the track five times, and record the time from A to B (t_{AB}) for each trial in Table 1.

2. Use the DataCollector in stopwatch mode to time the car from release to when the tab passes through the second photogate. The person operating the stopwatch should call out "1, 2, 3, GO!" On "Go!" the stopwatch operator should start the stopwatch, and the car operator should release the car. Then, the stopwatch operator should look straight on at photogate B and stop the stopwatch when the car's tab passes through the second photogate. Record times for five different trials in Table 1.

3. Tape a tongue depressor to the flag on the side of the car. Tape a paper plate to the tongue depressor. Use enough tape to make sure it is securely attached. You may need to slightly adjust photogate A so it isn't blocked by the tongue depressor, which is just a little wider than the car's tab.

4. Repeat steps 1 and 2, and record the photogate and stopwatch times in Table 1.

5. Find the average times, and record in Table 1.

Table 1: Car travel times

| Trial | Without sail | | With sail | |
	Photogate time A to B (s)	Stopwatch time A to B (s)	Photogate time A to B (s)	Stopwatch time A to B (s)
1				
2				
3				
4				
5				
Average				

4 Constructing explanations

a. Can you tell from the average times whether the sail had a significant effect on the car's motion? Why or why not?

b. How do your average times compare to your hypotheses from Part 1?

5 Analyzing the data

1. To find the estimated error in your measurements, find the difference between the average photogate time for the car without the sail and each of the individual trial times. Record absolute values (drop negative signs) in Table 2.

2. Calculate the average estimated error.

3. Repeat steps 1 and 2 for the stopwatch times for the car without the sail, and the photogate and stopwatch times for the car with the sail.

Table 2: Analyzing time data

Trial	Without sail		With sail	
	Estimated error photogate	Estimated error stopwatch	Estimated error photogate	Estimated error stopwatch
1				
2				
3				
4				
5				
Average estimated error				

Now you can compare estimated error with average times to see if the sail had a significant effect.

a. Find the difference between the average photogate times for the car with and without the sail. Compare this difference to the average estimated error for the photogate times with and without the sail. If the time difference is at least three times greater than the estimated error, you can conclude that the sail did change the motion of the car significantly. Based on your data, did the sail significantly change the motion of your car?

b. Find the difference between the average stopwatch times for the car with and without the sail. Compare this difference to the average estimated error for the stopwatch times with and without the sail. Is the time difference at least three times greater than the estimated error? Based on your data, did the sail significantly change the motion of your car?

6 Arguing from evidence

a. Reread the key question for this investigation. Answer the question using the evidence you collected to support your claim.

b. Describe one way you could improve this investigation so you can be even more sure that the change in the car's motion is due to air friction from the sail and not some other variable.

4C Studying Two-part Motion

What happens to the Energy Car as it travels down a hill and across a flat section of track?

In the previous Chapter 4 investigations, you explored the motion of the car on a flat track and on a hill. This time, you will put the track together so it has both a hill and a flat section. What will the speed vs. time graph look like? You will soon find out.

Materials

- CPO DataCollector and 2 photogates
- CPO Energy Car and Track
- CPO Physics Stand
- Steel marble

1 Making a prediction

You will set up the track so it has both an incline and a flat section. What will the speed vs. time graph look like?

a. Draw a sketch of what you think the speed vs. time graph will look like. Put *time* on the *x*-axis and *speed* on the *y*-axis.

2 Setting up the investigation

1. Join the steep incline and the flat section, and attach the track to the stand at the fourth hole from the bottom.
2. Place a stop at the top of the track with the plunger all the way back so the end is flush with the stop.
3. Place the other stop at the bottom of the track with a lump of clay on the plunger so the car won't bounce back through photogate B.
4. Attach photogate A as shown in the photo, and leave it there.
5. Photogate B will be placed every 5 centimeters, as shown in the photo.
6. *Make sure the flat part of the track is level.* Use the leveling feet on the Physics Stand base and on the bottom stop.
7. Place the Energy Car at the top of the track so it rests against the stop's plunger. Put one marble in the center of the car. Photogate B should be 5 centimeters from photogate A.

3 Doing the investigation

1. Put the DataCollector in CPO timer mode and select the interval function. Release the car and record the time through photogate A, the time through photogate B, the time from A to B, and the distance traveled in Table 1.

2. Move the photogate to the next 5-centimeter mark, and repeat step 1. Do this all along the track until you reach the last mark possible. You will not be able to take time measurements at 35, 40, or 45 centimeters from photogate A.

Table 1: Energy Car data

Distance A to B (cm)	Time A (s)	Time B (s)	Time AB (s)	Speed A (cm/s)	Speed B (cm/s)
5					
10					
15					
20					
25					
30					
50					
55					
60					
65					
70					
75					

4 Finding the speeds

a. Find the speed at A and the speed at B for each trial, and record in Table 1. Remember, to find the speed of the car, use the width of the flag (1 centimeter) for the distance and the time through the photogate for the time ($s = d/t$).

b. Look at the A speeds. What does this data tell you in general about the experiment?

c. Look at the B speeds. What does this data tell you in general about the motion of the car as it moved down the track? Draw a free-body diagram of the forces acting on the car.

5 Graphing the data

a. Create a speed vs. time graph for the data. Put *time AB* (s) on the *x*-axis and *speed at B* (cm/s) on the *y*-axis. Draw a best fit line.

b. How does the graph compare to your prediction? Explain.

6 Constructing explanations

a. Where is the car accelerating? Justify your answer with evidence from the experiment.

b. Where is the car moving at a constant speed? Justify your answer with evidence.

5C Gravity and Falling Objects

How does gravity affect the motion of falling objects?

Gravity causes objects to accelerate as they fall. An object is in *free fall* if it is moving under the influence of only gravity. For example, when you drop a ball, it is in free fall from the time it leaves your hand until it hits the ground. In this investigation, you will compare the motion of objects with different masses that are in free fall.

Materials

- CPO DataCollector and 2 photogates
- CPO Physics Stand
- Plastic ball and steel marbles
- Piece of string
- Tape

1 Setting up the investigation

1. This investigation should be done with the Physics Stand on the floor and with the pole as perfectly vertical as you can make it. Tape the steel marble to a piece of string to make a plumb bob. Hold the string at the top of the Physics Stand, and adjust the leveling feet until the string hangs down the center of the pole.

2. Attach photogate A near the top of the stand. The bottom of the U of the photogate should be against the pole.

3. Attach photogate B so it is 50 centimeters (10 holes) below photogate A.

4. Plug both photogates into the DataCollector; then remove the tape and string from the steel marble.

Centered   Parallel

When the pole is vertical, the string is centered and parallel.

2 Collecting data

1. Examine the photogates, and find the two small rectangular openings where the infrared light beam is emitted and detected. Hold the steel marble so it is above the top photogate, centered just above the openings.

2. Carefully drop the marble without giving it a push. Allow it to fall to the bottom of the stand, where one group member should catch it. The marble should fall straight through the center of the two photogates. This may take some practice.

Dropping the marble from photogate A

3. Put the DataCollector in CPO timer mode, and select the interval function. Record the time through photogate A (t_A), the time through photogate B (t_B), and the time from A to B (t_{AB}) in Table 1.

4. Repeat for a total of three trials with the steel marble.

5. Repeat for a total of three trials with the plastic marble.

Table 1: Photogate data

Marble	t_A (s)	t_B (s)	t_{AB} (s)
Steel			
Steel			
Steel			
Plastic			
Plastic			
Plastic			

3 Calculating acceleration

1. Calculate the speed of the marble through each photogate. The distance a marble moves when passing through the photogate is its diameter, 0.019 meters.

2. Use the two speeds and the time from A to B to calculate the acceleration for each trial.

Table 2: Speed and acceleration data

Marble	Speed through A (m/s)	Speed through B (m/s)	Acceleration (m/s^2)
Steel			
Steel			
Steel			
Plastic			
Plastic			
Plastic			

4 Analyzing the data

a. Calculate the average acceleration for your three trials for the steel marble. Use the average from each group in your class to find the class average for the steel marble's acceleration.

b. Calculate your average and the class average for the plastic marble's acceleration.

c. How do the accelerations compare? Are they about the same, or are they very different?

d. Which marble has the greater weight and is therefore pulled on by a stronger force of gravity?

e. Suppose you wanted to move the steel and plastic marbles across the floor with the same acceleration. Which would require more force to accelerate?

f. Use your answers from questions d and e to explain the accelerations of the two marbles in free fall. Draw a free-body diagram for each marble to illustrate your answer.

g. Why was it important to drop the marbles straight through the center of the photogate beam?

6C Collisions

Why do objects bounce back when they collide?

Newton's third law tells us that when two objects collide, they exert equal and opposite forces on each other. However, the effect of the force is not always the same. What happens when you collide two Energy Cars that have unequal masses?

Materials

- CPO Energy Car and Track
- CPO DataCollector and 2 photogates
- Thick rubber band
- Electronic scale (or triple-beam balance)

1 Making a collision

Launching the car

Rest your palm on the wood and pull the car against the screw with your finger on the tab nearest the far end of the car.

Moving car → Target car

1. Set up the long, straight track with a rubber band on one end and a clay ball on the other end. Use the bubble level to set the track level.

2. Place one steel marble in each car.

3. Wrap the thick rubber band around the target car. Place both cars on the track so their noses are pointed toward the rubber band launcher.

4. Place the target car near the center of the track. Use the screw to launch the other car, using the same deflection of the rubber band each time. The same force is applied to each launch. This car creates the collision.

5. To make a collision, release the moving car from the rubber band launcher. It will speed down the track and hit the target car. This is an efficient way to produce collisions on the track.

a. Does the *moving* car bounce back after the collision?

b. Does the *moving* car keep going forward after the collision?

c. Does the *moving* car stop at the collision?

d. How does the *target* car behave after the collision?

2 Constructing explanations

a. Describe in words the motion of the two cars before and after the collision.

b. The target car must exert a force on the moving car to stop it. How strong is this force relative to the force the moving car exerts on the target car to get it moving? How could you use the photogates to provide evidence for your answer?

3 Gathering evidence

Place photogates at 2 square marks near center of track.

1. Try the investigation again, but now use two photogates to collect time data.
2. Place two photogates on the square marks near the middle of the track.
3. Put the target car on the track so it is near photogate beam B.
4. Release the moving car from the rubber band launcher as before, and make a collision.
5. Repeat several times, and record trial times in Table 1.

Table 1: Collision times

Collision trial number	Time for moving car to pass through A before collision (s)	Time for target car to pass through B after collision (s)

167

a. Newton's third law tells us that when the moving car exerts a force on the target car, the target car exerts an equal and opposite force on the moving car. Does your data provide evidence for this? Explain.

b. You can compare times through A and B for each individual trial. How can using these times show there are equal and opposite forces at work?

4 Changing the masses

Moving car

0 marbles

2 marbles

Four combinations

Target car

0 marbles

2 marbles

Try the experiment with the four combinations of mass shown above. You do not need to use photogates for this part of the investigation. If you want to use photogates, you will have to use the memory button for several of the collisions. This is explained in the teacher's guide, and your teacher can provide guidance. If using photogates, create a new data table to record your results. Title your table.

5 Arguing from evidence

a. Describe the motion of the two cars when the target car has more mass than the moving car.

b. Describe the motion of the two cars when the target car has less mass than the moving car.

c. Explain how your observations support the law of equal and opposite action and reaction forces.

d. If the action and reaction forces are equal in strength, why does one car move at a different speed than the other after the collision when the masses are equal? (*Hint*: The answer involves Newton's second law.)

7C Energy and Efficiency

How efficiently is energy changed from one form to another?

All processes that involve energy exchanges lose small amounts of energy to friction and heat. Efficiency is a measure of how well energy is transformed from one kind to another or transferred from one object to another. A process that is 100 percent efficient is one in which no energy is "lost" or converted to forms such as heat or sound.

Materials

- CPO DataCollector and 2 photogates
- CPO Energy Car and Track
- 2 Rubber bands
- 3 Steel marbles
- Electronic scale (or triple-beam balance)

1 Setting up the investigation

Rubber band where car bounces

Rubber band that launches car

Level track

Photogate

1. Set up the long, straight track so it is level with rubber bands on both ends. The rubber bands should be twisted so they make an *X* in the middle.
2. Measure the mass of the empty car in kilograms, and record it in the first row of Table 1.
3. Place the car so it is at one end of the track, just touching the rubber band. Position a photogate so the car's flag will break the light beam right after the car moves away from the rubber band.
4. Place the car at the opposite end of the track from the photogate. Use the rubber band to launch the car toward the photogate. Measure the time the car takes to pass through the photogate before and after the car bounces off the rubber band. You will need to use the memory button to display the "before" time. Catch the car after the bounce.
5. Perform a couple of practice launches until you get consistent times. Record the before and after times, and calculate the average speeds before and after hitting the rubber bands.
6. Change the mass of the car by adding a marble. Repeat the procedure for a total of four trials, adding a marble and increasing mass each time.

Table 1: Bounce data for different masses

Mass of the car (including any marbles) (kg)	Time before bounce (s)	Speed before bounce (m/s)	Time after bounce (s)	Speed after bounce (m/s)

2 Constructing explanations

a. Describe how energy flows from the time when the car is launched until after the car bounces off the rubber band.

b. If the transformation of energy were perfect (100% efficiency), what would you expect the speed of the car to be before and after the bounce?

c. Calculate the kinetic energy of the car before and after bouncing off the rubber band for each trial. Record your answers in Table 2.

> **Useful relationships**
>
> $$\text{Kinetic energy} = \frac{1}{2}mv^2$$
>
> $$\text{Efficiency} = \frac{\text{Final energy}}{\text{Initial energy}}$$

d. Calculate the efficiency of the process of bouncing the car off a rubber band for each trial. Record your answers in Table 2.

e. Did the efficiency change when mass was added to the car? Describe any change you observed.

Table 2: Energy and efficiency data

Mass of car (kg)	Kinetic energy before bounce (J)	Kinetic energy after bounce (J)	Efficiency (%)

3 Changing a different variable

In the first part of the experiment, you investigated the effect of changing the car's mass on the efficiency. However, changing the mass also had the effect of changing the car's launch speed. In this part of the experiment, you will keep the mass constant and change only the car's speed.

1. Adjust the thumb screw so the rubber band stretches back only a small amount before touching the metal stopper. This will cause the car to launch at a slow speed. Launch the empty car, and record its time before and after the bounce off the rubber band at the other end of the track.

2. Twist the thumb screw so the rubber band stretches back a slightly greater distance. You will be doing four more launches, so adjust the screw so the stopper moves approximately one-fourth of the way back toward the wooden bumper. (Next time, the stopper should move halfway back, and so on.) Launch the car and measure the times. Record your readings in Table 3.

3. Continue until you have a total of five launches at different speeds. Use the recorded time data to calculate the speeds of the car. Record your calculations in Table 3.

Table 3: Bounce data for different speed

Mass of the car (kg)	Time before bounce (s)	Speed before bounce (m/s)	Time after bounce (s)	Speed after bounce (m/s)

4 Constructing explanations

a. Calculate the kinetic energy and efficiency of the rubber band for the different speeds you tested. Record the values in Table 4.

Table 4: Energy and efficiency data

Speed before bounce (m/s)	Speed after bounce (m/s)	Kinetic energy before bounce (J)	Kinetic energy after bounce (J)	Efficiency (%)

b. Plot a graph showing the efficiency on the vertical (*y*) axis and the speed before the bounce on the horizontal (*x*) axis. Does the speed of the car affect the efficiency? How?

171

8C People Power

What's your work and power as you climb a flight of stairs?

When you walk up a flight of stairs, you do work to lift your body against the force of gravity. If you know your weight and the vertical distance you climb, you can calculate the work you do. Measuring the time it takes to climb the stairs allows you to also calculate your power.

Materials

- CPO DataCollector or simple stopwatch
- Meter stick
- Bathroom scale

1 Collecting the data

1. You will be doing this activity as a class. Choose several students as volunteers who will climb a flight of stairs while others measure the time.

2. Use a bathroom scale to measure the weight of each volunteer. Convert each weight to newtons using the conversion factor: 1 pound = 4.448 newtons. Record each person's weight and name in Table 1.

Table 1: Stair climbing data

Name	Weight (N)	Stair height (m)	Time 1 (s)	Time 2 (s)	Time 3 (s)	Average time (s)

3. Choose three students to be timekeepers and two students to be stair height measurers. These should not be the same students who are climbing the stairs.

4. Locate an empty stairwell with one or two flights of stairs. The stair height measurers should measure the total vertical distance from the top to the bottom. The easiest way to do this is to measure the height of one stair, count the number of stairs, and multiply.

5. Have each person listed in Table 1 climb the stairs once while the three timekeepers measure the time. Record all three times in Table 1. Then, calculate the average time for each climber.

172

2 Calculating work and power

1. Calculate the work done by each person using this equation:
   Work (j) = Force (n) × distance (m). The force for each person is his or her weight.
   Record the work in Table 2.

2. Use each person's average time to calculate the power in watts:
   Power (w) = Work (j) ÷ time (s). Record each power in Table 2.

Table 2: Work and power

Name	Work (j)	Power (w)

3 Analyzing the data

a. Who did the most work? What do you notice about this person's weight?

b. Who did the least work? What do you notice about this person's weight?

c. Who had the greatest power? Must this be the person with the fastest time?

d. Who had the least power? Must this be the person with the slowest time?

e. Calculate the average work done by the climbers.

f. The calorie is also a unit of work. One calorie equals 4,186 joules. Calculate the average number of calories of work done by the climbers. You may be surprised at how small the number is!

g. Calculate the average power of the climbers.

h. A typical bright light bulb has a power of 100 watts. How does this compare to the average power of the climbers?

i. Suppose two people of equal weights climb the same flight of stairs. One runs, and the other walks. Do they burn the same number of calories? Do they have the same power? Explain.

j. Juan's weight is twice that of his little sister Anna. They climb the same flights of stairs and have the same power. Explain how this can be possible.

9C Mechanical Advantage

What is mechanical advantage, and how do ropes and pulleys give you mechanical advantage?

Ropes and pulleys produce large output forces from small input forces—but how large can the output forces be? What is the trade-off? In this investigation, you will explore the mechanical advantage of different rope and pulley setups. You will also discover a simple way to determine the mechanical advantage of any rope and pulley system.

Materials

- Top and bottom pulley blocks
- CPO Physics Stand
- 4 Weights
- Spring scale (0–10 N)
- Yellow string with brass clip and cord stops
- 2 Knobs (1 threaded, 1 regular)

1 Setting up the investigation

Top block

One supporting string (clip to bottom)

Bottom block

Attach spring scale hook to cord stop this way. Pull gently and slowly to see how much input force you need to lift the bottom block.

1. Attach four weights to the bottom block. Use a spring scale to measure the weight (N) of the bottom block, and record it in Table 1 as the *output force*.

2. Attach the top block near the top of the Physics Stand.

3. Thread the yellow string over one or more of the pulleys of the top and bottom pulley blocks. The yellow string can be clipped to either the top block or the bottom block.

4. Build combinations with 1, 2, 3, 4, 5, and 6 strands directly supporting the bottom block so that you always pull down on the string to raise the block. (*Hint*: 1, 3, and 5 have the string clipped to the bottom block; 2, 4, and 6 have the string clipped to the top block.)

5. Attach the spring scale to the cord stop on the string as shown in the photo. This way of sliding the spring scale hook over the cord stop will give the best force measurement. If you insert the hook into the hole of the cord stop, some friction will interfere with the measurement.

6. Use a spring scale to measure the force needed to slowly lift the bottom block for different combinations of supporting strings.

Safety Tip: Don't pull sideways; the stand might tip over!

Table 1: Rope and pulley force data

Number of supporting strings	Input force (N)	Output force (N)	Output force ÷ Input force
1			
2			
3			
4			
5			
6			

2 Mechanical advantage

a. Mechanical advantage refers to the number of times effort or input force is multiplied in a simple machine like a rope and pulley system. The ratio of output force to input force equals the mechanical advantage, so divide output force by input force for each trial then record your results in Table 2. *Mechanical advantage has no unit; it is a ratio.*

b. What is the relationship between number of supporting strings and mechanical advantage?

c. The mechanical advantage for your first trial is 1. Since any number multiplied by 1 equals the same number, your input force is not multiplied. What could the advantage be for using only one supporting string? (*Hint*: This arrangement is often used to raise a flag on a flagpole.)

d. A windjammer is a large sailing ship that was popular in the 1700s and 1800s. Now, tourists enjoy sailing on reproductions like the one in the photo. Rope and pulley systems (called blocks and tackles) are used to lift the sails, which can require a lot of force in a strong wind! What is the mechanical advantage of a windjammer's rope and pulley system for one of its sails if there are five supporting lines?

3 Input and output distances

Rope and pulley systems with a mechanical advantage greater than 1 will reduce the amount of force you have to put into the machine to make it work. However, this multiplied effort force comes at a "cost." What is the trade-off?

1. Use the marker stop (cord stop) to mark where the string leaves the top pulley.

2. Choose a distance that you will lift the bottom pulley during each trial of the experiment. This is the *output distance*. Your output distance should be at least 20 centimeters.

3. Pull the yellow string to lift the block your chosen distance.

4. Measure how much string length you had to pull to lift the block. This is the *input distance*.

Set both cord stops near the top pulley before pulling the string.

Slide one cord stop up after pulling the string.

String length (L)

(h)

Height difference for block

Measuring string length and height difference

5. Measure the input and output distances for each of the different configurations: 1, 2, 3, 4, 5, and 6. Table 2 shows only two data rows; create a complete data table in your notebook.

Table 2: Rope and pulley distance data

Mechanical advantage	Input distance (cm)	Output distance (cm)
1		
2		

a. Study the data in Table 2. What is the "cost" for having a mechanical advantage greater than 1?

b. You can calculate mechanical advantage using input and output distances instead of forces. From the data in Table 2, figure out a new way to calculate the mechanical advantage of a rope and pulley system.

c. Windjammers usually have two to five masts with sails. Suppose one sail weighs 3,000 N and is rigged with a rope and pulley system that has five supporting lines. The sail must be raised 35 meters. How much line will be needed to raise this sail?

10C Freezing Point of a Stable Mixture

What is the freezing point of a unique ice cream topping?

Have you ever put shell topping on a frozen desert like ice cream? The topping is a liquid in the plastic bottle, but when you put it on ice cream, it hardens very quickly to form a shell or crust over the dessert. The ice cream topping contains lecithin, a substance that stabilizes the mixture, so it acts like a pure substance when heated or cooled. In this investigation, you will compare the freezing points of different shell topping brands.

Materials
- Shell ice cream topping
- Foam cup (large)
- Large glass or plastic test tube
- CPO DataCollector
- Temperature probe
- Ice water

1 Doing the investigation

1. Fill a foam cup about three-quarters full with ice water.
2. Shake the bottle of ice cream topping well, and pour about 15 milliliters into the test tube. This step might already have been completed for you.
3. Place the temperature probe in the test tube.
4. Connect the temperature probe to the DataCollector, and set up a new investigation. Choose a sample rate of 5 seconds per sample. This means temperature data will be taken and placed in the table every 5 seconds.
5. Start the DataCollector. Place the test tube into the ice water bath. Use the temperature probe to gently stir the mixture while the temperature data is collected. Continue stirring until the topping is a solid and you can't move the thermometer anymore. Once the topping is a solid, continue collecting data until the temperature reaches 4 or 5°C (the temperature of the ice water bath).
6. Save the DataCollector experiment, and make a note of the file name.
7. Follow your teacher's instructions for cleanup.

2 Analyzing the data

Go to the graph screen on your DataCollector. The graph should show temperature on the *y*-axis and time on the *x*-axis. If this is not the case, select the correct variable for each axis. Study the graph and answer these questions.

a. As you cooled the mixture, what happened to the temperature at first?

b. At some point in the cooling process, you will see that the line on the graph is relatively flat (this is called a plateau). What does this tell you about the temperature during this time period?

c. What is happening to the ice cream topping during this part of the cooling process?

177

d. Did the temperature drop again after the plateau? Discuss. On a piece of graph paper, sketch the graph on your DataCollector. You do not have to use numbers, but you should label each axis with the correct variable and the area of the graph where freezing occurred. Make a note of the average temperature (freezing point). Or, you can download the data to a spreadsheet and create a graph to print and place in your notebook.

3 Constructing explanations

Different brands of shell ice cream topping have similar ingredients, but they are not all identical. Are their compositions different enough to affect the freezing point? You will compare results with other groups to find out.

a. Based on your data analysis, at what temperature did your brand or type of shell topping freeze?

b. Compare your freezing point with that of other groups that tested the same brand. Is the temperature similar? Discuss.

c. Compare your freezing point with that of other groups that tested a different brand or type of topping. Is the temperature similar? Discuss.

d. Based on your observations, if your teacher gave you an unknown brand of shell topping, would you be able to identify the brand or type by finding its freezing point? Explain your answer.

4 Arguing from evidence

a. When the topping was in the ice water bath, thermal energy was transferred away from the topping. At first, the temperature dropped rapidly, and then the temperature leveled off. Why?

b. What would shell topping be like if the freezing point was 20°C?

c. What would shell topping be like if the freezing point was 0°C?

d. Pure substances have unique freezing/melting points, but mixtures generally do not. Shell topping is a mixture that *does* freeze and melt within a certain temperature range. Why does the topping act like a pure substance?

11C Mass Determination Without a Balance

Can the mass of an object be determined without the use of a balance?

The mass of an object is the amount of matter in that object. This physical property can easily be measured with the use of a common piece of laboratory equipment: a balance. How could you determine the mass of a pure substance if the balance was out of order?

Materials

- Foam cup
- Metal sample
- Hot plate
- Tongs
- Safety goggles
- Balance
- 100-mL Graduated cylinder
- CPO DataCollector
- Temperature probe
- ~600 mL water
- Lab apron
- 400-mL Beaker
- Heat mitt

The following table of specific heat values will be useful:

Name of substance	Specific heat (J/g°C)
Aluminum	0.899
Brass	0.38
Copper	0.38
Nickel	0.443
Iron	0.46
Steel	0.46
Water	4.18
Zinc	0.388

1 Analyzing and interpreting data

When choosing a material to serve as an insulator, should you pick a material with a high specific heat or a low specific heat? Explain your answer.

2 Doing the investigation

1. Use the hot plate to heat 200 milliliters of water in the beaker until the water boils. Gently lower the metal sample into the beaker using the tongs. Allow the sample to settle in the boiling water for 2 to 3 minutes so its temperature will be equal to that of the boiling water.
2. While the metal is warming in the water, begin to set up the calorimeter.
3. Measure exactly 100.0 milliliters of room temperature water in a graduated cylinder, and pour the water into the foam cup. Record this volume in the Table 1.
4. Measure and record the stabilized temperature of the water in Table 1.

179

5. After 2 to 3 minutes have passed, measure the temperature of the boiling water with the temperature probe, and record this value in Table 1.

6. Using the tongs, carefully remove the metal from the boiling water and quickly transfer it to the calorimeter.

7. Stir the water in the calorimeter carefully with the temperature probe.

8. Watch the temperature reading as you stir. When the temperature reaches a plateau (no longer increases), record the temperature of the metal-water system in Table 1, stop stirring, and remove the metal.

9. Repeat the procedure for trial 2, replacing the water in the calorimeter with fresh water.

Table 1: Determining mass data

	Trial 1	Trial 2
V_{H2O} in calorimeter (mL)		
T_i of H_2O in calorimeter (°C)		
T_i of metal in hot water (°C)		
T_f of system (°C)		
Mass of metal (g)		

3 Analyzing the data

A. Calculate the heat absorbed by the water.

1. Find the mass (m_1) of the original volume of water using V_{H2O} and density.
2. Find the change in temperature of the water using $\Delta T = T_f - T_i$.
3. Find the heat energy absorbed by the water (Q_{H2O}) using $Q_{H2O} = mC_p\Delta T$.

B. Calculate the mass of the metal.

1. Find the change in temperature of the metal using $\Delta T = T_f - T_i$.
2. Find the heat energy released by the metal (Q_{metal}) using $-Q_{metal} = Q_{H2O}$.
3. Find the mass of the metal (m) using $Q_{metal} = mC_p\Delta T$.
4. Perform all calculations up to this point for both trial 1 and trial 2, then average your two mass predictions and use your average mass value for the calculation in step 6.
5. Use the balance to measure the mass of your metal sample. This is the "real" value for the calculation in step 6.
6. Percent error, where % error $= \dfrac{experimental - real}{real} \times 100$

4 Constructing explanations

a. A sample of nickel is found to absorb 4.25 kilojoules as it is heated from 15.0°C to 37.5°C. What is the mass of this nickel sample?

b. Predict how your experiment results would differ if you allowed your metal to stay in the boiling water for only 2 minutes. Explain.

c. Name two possible sources of error for this experiment. How would they affect your data? How would they affect your results?

12C Density of Fluids

What is the maximum load a boat can hold before sinking? How is the maximum load affected by the density of the water in which the boat floats?

In Investigation 12B, you designed and created a clay boat that floated in water. You learned that the density of the boat should be equal to or less than the water in order to float. You also saw that altering the shape of the clay changed its ability to float. In this investigation, you will work to see what element of boat design increases the maximum load that your boat can handle before sinking, and explore how this relates to the density of water.

Materials

- Modeling clay (same amount as in Inv. 12B)
- Metal washers or pennies
- Water
- Shallow pan or bucket
- Displacement tank
- 100-mL Graduated cylinder
- 250-mL Beaker for overflow
- Electronic scale (or triple-beam balance)
- Salt
- Paper towels or sponges
- Disposable cup to catch displaced water when filling tank

1 Making a prediction

a. What element of design do you think will affect the amount of weight your boat can hold without sinking? Explain.

2 Finding the apparent density of your clay boat

1. Form your clay into a floating boat like the one you made in Investigation 12B.

2. Find the total volume of the clay boat. This means the sum of the volumes of the clay itself and the empty air space of the boat. Record your values in Table 1.

   a. Measure the volume of your clay boat by displacement.

   b. Measure the volume of your boat's empty air space. Start by filling a 100-milliliter graduated cylinder with water up to the 100-milliliter line. Pour water from the cylinder into your boat until it completely fills up. Once it is full, see how much water is left in the graduated cylinder. Subtract that amount from the 100 milliliters you started with to determine the volume of air space.

   c. Calculate the total volume of the clay boat.

Step B

Start with 100 mL.

Fill your boat with water.

Calculate the difference between 100 mL and what is left in the cylinder.

3. Measure the mass of the boat.
4. Calculate the apparent density of your clay boat (mass/total volume).

Table 1: Volume, mass, and density data

Volume of clay used in boat (mL)	Volume of empty space (mL)	Total volume of clay boat (mL)	Mass of boat (g)	Apparent density of your boat (g/mL)

3 Predicting the maximum load of the boat

The boat will sink once it becomes denser than the water. You are going to predict the maximum load for your boat based on the data you collected in Table 1. To do this, you will come up with a mathematical relationship that enables you to solve for the maximum load. Start by looking at your boat's apparent density and the density it must remain less than to stay afloat.

a. What is the mass of your boat?

b. What is the total volume of your boat?

c. What is your boat's apparent density?

d. What is the maximum apparent density your boat can attain and still remain afloat?

e. Where would the additional mass of the load your boat carries enter into the apparent density calculation?

f. Write an equation to calculate the apparent density of your boat when carrying a load.

g. Solve your equation for maximum load. What is your calculated maximum load?

4 Testing the theoretical value

1. Place your boat in the water.
2. Record your calculated maximum load in Table 2.
3. Add one washer at a time to your boat. Once the boat starts to sink, stop adding washers, and measure the total mass of the washers your boat successfully carried. Record this value in Table 2.
4. Find the percent error, and record this value in Table 2.
5. Who in the class was able to carry the largest load? Look at his or her design and the designs of others. What design characteristics do the most successful boats share?

Table 2: Maximum load data for fresh water

Calculated maximum load (g)	Measured maximum load (g)	Percent error of calculated maximum load

5 Changing the density of the liquid

The Dead Sea is located in the Middle East between Jordan to the east, and Israel and the West Bank to the west. It is known for its dense salt water. Would your boat have the same maximum capacity if it were in very salty water with a much higher density than the fresh water you've used so far?

1. You will need to find the density of the salt water. Find the mass of 100 milliliters of the saltwater solution by using a graduated cylinder. Record the mass in Table 3.

2. Calculate the density of the saltwater sample. Record the density in Table 3.

3. Use your equation from Part 3 to calculate the maximum load for your boat in the saltwater solution. Record this value in Table 3.

4. Test the maximum load in the salt water solution. Record the value in Table 3.

5. Find the percent error, and record in Table 3.

Table 3: Maximun load data for saltwater solution

Mass of saltwater sample (g)	Density of saltwater sample (g/mL)	Calculated maximum load (g)	Measured maximum load (g)	Percent error of calculated maximum load

6 Constructing explanations

a. In order for a boat to carry more weight, what element of the boat design needs to be changed? Explain.

b. As water density increases, can a boat hold more or less weight? Why?

c. Explain any differences in the percent errors you found for the fresh water and the salt water.

d. In an estuary, salt water from the ocean and fresh water from a river meet. What would you expect to happen with these waters in the estuary? Would there be any stratification?

e. Research to find the average density of a typical sample of ocean water. How does this density compare to fresh water and to the sample that modeled the Dead Sea? Would your boat hold more or fewer washers in fresh water and in typical ocean water than in Dead Sea water?

13C Charles's Law

What is the relationship between the volume and temperature of a gas?

Jacques Charles (1746–1823) determined the relationship between temperature and volume for an enclosed gas. In this simple investigation, you will measure the volume of air in a balloon, heat the system, and observe and collect temperature and volume data as the system cools. From this data, you will be able to derive Charles's law.

Materials

- Balloon
- Plunger assembly
- Displacement tank
- Tray or dish pan
- Ice
- Temperature probe
- CPO DataCollector
- Foam cup

1 Modeling temperature and volume

a. If you inflate a balloon and leave it on a sunny windowsill, what do you think will happen to the balloon?

b. Make a hypothesis about the relationship between volume and temperature of an enclosed gas. (*Hint*: When temperature increases, what do you think happens to the volume?)

2 Setting up the experiment

1. To begin making the plunger assembly, use the weights base that comes with the equipment kit. Remove all the steel weights (you won't need them).

2. Cut a foam cup so that it is 12 centimeters high, then make a small hole in the side of the cup.

3. Poke a hole in the bottom of the cup using one of the posts, and leave the cup attached to the weights base as shown in the photo. You will use this plunger assembly to submerge the balloon in the displacement tank.

Weights base

Slide cup onto post.

12 cm

Cup fits over post.

Foam cup

4. Blow up a balloon but don't tie it. Allow it to deflate. Repeat this process three times. This will stretch the balloon so it is easier to use in experiment.

5. Blow up the balloon with enough air so that it will fit easily, *not* snugly, in the displacement tank (approximately 12 centimeters in diameter).

185

3 Doing the experiment

1. Set the displacement tank on a tray or dish pan. Add 1,250 milliliters of ice water to the tank.

2. Submerge the balloon completely by pushing down on it with the plunger assembly. Water will flow out of the tank spout into the pan. If it does not, add water until some runs out.

Plunger assembly

Water level up to overflow point

Balloon

Container to catch overflow water

3. Place the temperature probe in the displacement tank. Wait for one minute, then record the temperature in Table 1. If the water level has decreased and is no longer on the verge of overflowing, fill the tank with the same temperature water until it starts to overflow.

4. Remove the weights base/foam cup assembly and balloon.

5. Record the displaced volume of water by referring to the scale on the side of the displacement tank labeled Displaced Volume. Record the values in Table 1.

6. Empty the displacement tank until the water level reads 750 milliliters. Then add warm water until the level again reaches 1,250 milliliters.

Tank volume

Displacement volume

900 mL displaced

1000 mL of water in tank

This scale shows how much water is in the displacement tank.

This scale shows how much water was displaced.

7. Check the temperature of the tank water. It should be about 10–15°C warmer than in the previous trial. Adjust the water temperature if necessary by adding ice or warm water.

8. Repeat steps 2–7 until you have at least four data points.

9. Find the volume of the balloon for each trial by subtracting the tank volume from 1,900 milliliters (which is the total tank volume). Record in Table 1.

10. Convert Celsius temperatures to Kelvin temperatures, and record in Table 1.

Table 1: Volume and temperature data

Tank volume (mL)	Volume of the balloon and plunger as read from tank (mL)	Temperature (°C)	Temperature (Kelvin)	V*T (mL*K)	V/T (mL/K)

4 Graphing the data

Use your data to make a graph of volume vs. temperature.

a. Does the graphical model support your hypothesis? Explain your answer.

b. What happens to the volume of an enclosed gas when the temperature increases?

5 Finding a relationship between volume and temperature

a. Divide the volume and temperature values for each trial, and record the answers in Table 1. Remember to use the correct number of significant digits.

b. Multiply the volume by the temperature for each trial, and record the values in Table 1. Again, use the correct number of significant digits.

c. The mathematical relationship between volume and temperature always equals a constant value. Based on your calculations, is that relationship V/T or $V \times T$?

d. According to your data, what is the constant value? (You can record an average.)

6 Using Charles's law to make a prediction

a. Using your constant value, calculate the volume of the balloon and plunger assembly when the temperature is 290 K. (Use a similar temperature if this is already one of your data points.)

b. Using your graph, what volume corresponds to 290 K? How does this compare to your calculated value?

c. How would you use the experiment setup to test your predicted volume value for 290 K?

7 Constructing explanations

a. If you do this experiment with much hotter water (such as 60°C), the balloon/plunger volume measurements should increase, but they don't. Why do you think this is so? (*Hint*: Think about the way the experiment is set up.)

b. Go back to your answer to question 1a. Would you answer the question the same way now? Explain.

14C Energy and the Quantum Theory

How do atoms absorb and emit light energy?

The electrons in an atom are organized into energy levels. You can think of energy levels like a staircase—an electron can be on one step or another but not between steps. When an electron changes levels, the atom absorbs or emits energy, often in the form of light. This investigation will teach you a challenging and fun game that simulates how atoms exchange energy through light. The process is fundamentally how a laser works.

Materials

• CPO Atom Building Game

1 The neon atom

1. Build a neon atom with 10 each of protons (red or green marbles), neutrons (blue marbles) and electrons (yellow marbles).

2. Set the electrons in the lowest spaces possible.

3. Find the following cards in the Photons and Lasers can:
   Pump 1 (red)
   Pump 2 (yellow)
   Laser 1 (red)

Neon-20 (Ne^{20})

10 protons, 10 neutrons, 10 electrons

2 How atoms exchange energy

a. Explain the meaning of the term *ground state* when applied to an atom.

b. Can the second energy level of neon hold any more electrons? How does this affect neon's chemical properties and position on the periodic table?

c. Put a red pump 1 card on the atom board. Move one electron from level 2 to level 3. Explain what this sequence of actions represents in a real atom.

d. Put a yellow pump 2 card on the atom board. Move any one electron up two levels. Explain what this sequence of actions represents in a real atom.

e. Put a red laser 1 card on the atom board. Move any one electron down one level. Explain what this sequence of actions represents in a real atom.

3 The photons and lasers game

Photons and lasers card deck

Pump cards
Add energy to the atom and advance electrons up levels

Laser cards
Release energy from the atom and drop electrons down levels

1. The first player to reach 10 points wins the game.

2. Each player starts with five cards and plays one per turn, drawing a new card to maintain a hand of five.

A **Laser-2** card can drop this electron 2 levels scoring 2 points

3. Playing a pump card allows the player to advance one electron up by the number of levels shown on the card (1–4). No points are scored by playing pump cards.

4. Playing a laser card allows the player to drop electrons from one level to a lower level. The player scores one point per electron per level. For example, moving two electrons down two levels scores four points.

5. Rules for playing laser cards:
   Electrons can be moved down only if there are empty states for them to move to.
   Electrons can be moved from only one level in a turn.
   If the card says Laser-2, then each electron must move down two levels.

4 Constructing explanations

a. What does the term *excited state* mean with respect to energy and atoms?

b. What physical principle prevents two electrons from moving into the same state?

c. Arrange the following colors of light in order of increasing energy: blue, red, green, yellow.

d. Could an atom emit one photon of blue light after absorbing only one photon of red light? Explain why or why not.

e. Suppose a real atom had energy levels just like the game. Could this atom make blue-green light with an energy in between blue and green? Explain what colors this atom could make.

15C Activity Series of Metals

How reactive are different metals?

An activity series is a list of elements arranged from most reactive to least reactive. When you place a solid piece of metal in contact with a solution, there may or may not be a reaction. In order for a reaction to occur, the solid metal that is touching the solution must be more reactive than the metal that is part of the ionic compound (solute) dissolved in the water. In this investigation, you will examine several metals and rank them from most to least active based on how many reactions take place for each metal.

Materials

- Well plate (5 × 5) or overhead (lead acetate sheet)
- Copper solid
- Zinc solid
- Lead solid
- Magnesium solid
- Forceps
- Eyedroppers
- Safety goggles
- Safety apron, protective gloves

- $Mg(NO_3)_2$ solution
- $Zn(NO_3)_2$ solution
- $Pb(NO_3)_2$ solution
- $AgNO_3$ solution
- $Cu(NO_3)_2$ solution

1 Making a prediction

Of the four metals in the materials list, which do you think will be the most reactive?

2 Doing the investigation

1. You will need a 5-by-5 well plate. It will be arranged similar to the layout of Table 1. With an eyedropper, place 7 drops of each solution into each of four wells. For example, place 7 drops of $Cu(NO_3)_2$ solution in each of four wells across the top of the well plate.

2. If you are using a clear plastic well plate, place a sheet of white paper under it so you can see evidence of a potential chemical reaction more easily.

3. Place one sample of each metal into each solution using forceps. For example, place one sample of copper in the first well of the row containing the $Cu(NO_3)_2$ solution. Then place a sample of copper into the first well of the row containing $Zn(NO_3)_2$, and so on, until the first well in each row has a sample of copper in it. Repeat this process, placing one sample of zinc in each of the second wells in each row, lead in the third, and magnesium in the fourth.

Putting drops
in wells

**Do not use bare
hands to place metal
samples in well!**

4. After 15 minutes, use forceps to examine each metal. Be sure to turn the metal over and look at the underside for evidence of a chemical reaction.

5. Place an *X* in any square of Table 1 where a reaction occurs.

6. Clean up according to your teacher's directions. Be sure to wash your hands.

7. Add up the number of *X*s for each metal as earlier, and write the total in Table 1.

Table 1: Reactivity data

	Cu	Zn	Pb	Mg
$Cu(NO_3)_2$				
$Zn(NO_3)_2$				
$Pb(NO_3)_2$				
$Mg(NO_3)_2$				
$AgNO_3$				

Metal	Cu	Zn	Pb	Mg
Number of reactions				

3 Constructing explanations

a. What evidence of chemical reactions did you observe in this experiment?

b. Rank the four solid metals used in the experiment from most reactive to least reactive.

c. Even though silver solid was not used here, make a judgment as to where it would rank in this activity series. Explain.

d. Compare the activity series you just constructed with one provided by your teacher. How do they compare?

16C Carbon and Its Chemistry

What are some common molecules that contain carbon?

Living organisms are made up of a great variety of molecules, but the number of different elements involved is very small. Organic chemistry is the science of molecules that contain carbon, and these are the ones most important to living organisms. This investigation introduces you to some small organic molecules.

Materials
- CPO Periodic Table Tiles
- Reference book of organic compounds

1 The chemistry of carbon

Carbon is the key element in the chemistry of living things. This is because carbon can make complex molecules. Each carbon atom can make four bonds because carbon has four electrons in its outer energy level, which can hold a total of eight. Carbon can also form double and triple bonds by sharing two or three electrons with a single atom. Because of carbon's flexible bonding ability, many molecular structures are possible.

Straight chains

```
  H  H  H
  |  |  |
H-C--C--C-H
  |  |  |
  H  H  H
```
Propane
C_3H_8

Branched chains

```
            H
          H-C-H
  H  H  H  |  H
  |  |  |  |  |
H-C--C--C--C--C-H
  |  |  |  |  |
  H  |  H  |  H
  H-C-H H-C-H
    H     H
```
Iso-octane
C_8H_{18}

Rings

```
        H
        |
        C
   H   / \\   H
    \\ C   C /
     |     ||
     C     C
    / \\   / \\
   H   C   H
       |
       H
```
Benzene
C_6H_6

2 Single-carbon molecules

Carbon dioxide
CO_2

Methyl alcohol (methanol)
CH_3OH

Methane
CH_4

1. Build the three carbon molecules above using the Periodic Table Tiles.
2. Build a model of carbonic acid: H_2CO_3.

3 Analyzing and interpreting data

a. Research and describe at least one use of methyl alcohol.

b. Research and describe the production and use of methane.

4 Two-carbon molecules

Once a molecule has two carbon atoms, the structures get more complicated. The carbon atoms may share a single, double, or triple bond between them.

Acetic acid
CH_3COOH

Ethane
C_2H_6

1. Build the two-carbon molecules above using the Periodic Table Tiles.
2. Build a model of ethyl alcohol (ethanol): C_2H_5OH. (*Hint*: Each carbon atom makes four bonds, and the oxygen atom makes two bonds.)
3. Build a model of acetylene: C_2H_2. (*Hint*: There is a triple bond between the two carbon atoms.)

5 Analyzing and interpreting data

a. Research and describe where acetic acid is found.

b. Research and describe at least one use of ethyl alcohol.

6 Biological molecules

Living organisms are constructed mainly of proteins, which are very large carbon-based molecules, such as hemoglobin (right). A single protein may contain 10,000 or more atoms. Proteins themselves are constructed of simpler units called amino acids. For example, the hemoglobin molecule contains 584 amino acids.

Hemoglobin molecule

Use the Periodic Table Tiles to build models of the three smallest amino acids.

$$H\diagdown \atop H\diagup N - \overset{\overset{H}{|}}{\underset{\underset{H}{|}}{C}} - \overset{\overset{O}{\|}}{C} - O - H$$

Glycine

$$H\diagdown \atop H\diagup N - \overset{\overset{H}{|}}{\underset{\underset{H-\overset{|}{C}-H}{|}}{C}} - \overset{\overset{O}{\|}}{C} - O - H$$

Alanine H

$$H\diagdown \atop H\diagup N - \overset{\overset{H}{|}}{\underset{\underset{H-\overset{|}{C}-H}{|}}{C}} - \overset{\overset{O}{\|}}{C} - O - H$$

Serine O−H

7 Analyzing and interpreting data

a. What is similar about all three amino acids shown above?

b. Is the chemical diagrammed on the right an amino acid? Explain why you think so.

$$H\diagdown \atop H\diagup N - \overset{\overset{H}{|}}{\underset{\underset{H-\overset{|}{C}-H}{|}}{C}} - \overset{\overset{O}{\|}}{C} - O - H$$

$O - C - O - H$

Is this an amino acid?

193

17C Classifying Chemical Reactions

How can you predict the products of a chemical reaction?

In a previous investigation, you learned to balance chemical equations. You may have noticed some patterns in those reactions. For example, you balanced some reactions in which a carbon compound reacted with oxygen gas to produce carbon dioxide and water. In this investigation, you will explore similar patterns and learn how they can help you predict the products of a chemical reaction.

Materials

- CPO Periodic Table Tiles

1 Addition reactions

When two substances combine to form one new substance, we call the reaction an *addition reaction*. The general formula for an addition reaction is A + B → AB. The sodium-chlorine addition reaction built using the Periodic Table Tiles looks like this:

2 Decomposition reactions

When one substance breaks down to form two substances, we call the reaction a *decomposition reaction*. The general formula for a decomposition reaction is AB → A + B. The water decomposition reaction built using the Periodic Table Tiles looks like this:

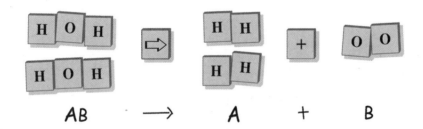

3 Single-displacement reactions

A third type of reaction, called a *single-displacement reaction*, occurs when one element replaces a similar element in a compound. If you put an iron nail into a beaker of copper chloride, you will see reddish copper forming on the nail.

Reactants

Fe   Cu Cl₂

Products

Fe Cl₂   Cu

Iron replaces copper in the solution, and copper falls out of the solution as a metal: $CuCl_2 + Fe \rightarrow FeCl_2 + Cu$. The general formula for a single-displacement reaction is $AX + B \rightarrow BX + A$.

4 Double-displacement reactions

A *double-displacement* reaction occurs when ions from two compounds in a solution switch places to form two new compounds. This happens in the reaction between hydrochloric acid and sodium hydroxide: $NaOH + HCl \rightarrow NaCl + H_2O$. The general formula for a double-displacement reaction is $AB + CD \rightarrow AD + CB$.

Solution A

Solution B

Precipitate

5 Combustion reactions

A fifth type of chemical reaction occurs when something burns. We call these reactions *combustion reactions*. You are probably familiar with combustion reactions in which a carbon compound is burned to produce carbon dioxide and water.

Reactants

O_2

O_2

CH_4

Products

H_2O

H_2O

CO_2

For example, methane (natural gas) is burned to heat homes:

$$CH_4 + 2O_2 \rightarrow CO_2 + 2H_2O$$

The general formula for a carbon combustion

reaction is: **carbon compound** $+ O_2 \rightarrow CO_2 + H_2O$.

Carbon Compound $+$ O_2 $\longrightarrow$ CO_2 $+$ H_2O

6 Summary of types of reactions

Table 1: Types of chemical reactions

Type	General equation	Example
Addition	A + B → AB	$2Na + Cl_2 \rightarrow 2NaCl$
Decomposition	AB → A + B	$2H_2O \rightarrow 2H_2 + O_2$
Single-displacement	AX + B → BX + A	$CuCl_2 + Fe \rightarrow FeCl_2 + Cu$
Double-displacement	AB + CD → AD +CB	$HCl + NaOH \rightarrow NaCl + H_2O$
Combustion	carb cpd $+ O_2 \rightarrow CO_2 + H_2O$	$CH_4 + 2O_2 \rightarrow CO_2 + 2H_2O$

7 Predicting the products of a chemical reaction

Using Table 1, predict the products of these chemical reactions.

a. The addition of magnesium and iodine: $Mg + I_2 \rightarrow ?$

b. The decomposition of mercury oxide: $HgO \rightarrow ?$

c. In potassium nitrate, the potassium is replaced by lead: $KNO_3 + Pb \rightarrow ?$

d. The reaction between hydrochloric acid and potassium hydroxide: $HCl + KOH \rightarrow ?$

e. The combustion of liquid hexane: $C_6H_{14} + O_2 \rightarrow ?$

8 Balancing equations given only the reactants

Use the Periodic Table Tiles to help you complete and balance the following chemical equations.

a. $Al + Br_2 \rightarrow$

b. $KBr + Cl_2 \rightarrow$

c. $HCl + K_2SO_3 \rightarrow$

d. $C_2H_6 + O_2 \rightarrow$

e. $Al_2O_3 \rightarrow$

f. $ZnSO_4 + SrCl_2 \rightarrow$

g. $Mg + HCl \rightarrow$

h. $CaCl_2 \rightarrow$

i. $C_5H_{12} + O_2 \rightarrow$

j. $Sb + I_2 \rightarrow$

18C Nuclear Reactions

How do we model nuclear reactions?

You would be very surprised to see a bus spontaneously transform into three cars and a motorcycle. But radioactive atoms do something very similar. If left alone, a radioactive atom eventually turns into another kind of atom, with completely different properties. This investigation looks at some basic concepts behind radioactivity.

Materials

- CPO Atom Building Game
- 50 Pennies
- Cup
- Graph paper

1 Radioactivity

Heads

Tails

Set 50 pennies heads up on the desk.

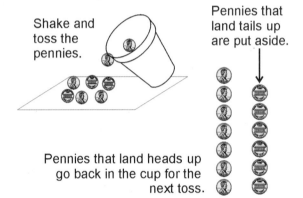

Shake and toss the pennies.

Pennies that land tails up are put aside.

Pennies that land heads up go back in the cup for the next toss.

1. Place 50 pennies in a paper cup, shake them and dump them on the table. Each penny represents an atom of carbon-14.

2. Separate the pennies that land tails up. Count the heads-up pennies and tails-up pennies, and record the number of each in Table 1 in the row for the first toss.

3. Put *only the pennies that landed heads up* back in the cup. Put the tails-up pennies aside. Shake the cup again and dump the pennies on the table.

4. Record the number of heads-up pennies in the row for the second toss.

5. Repeat the experiment using only the pennies that land heads up until you have one or no pennies left.

Table 1: Coin toss decay simulation

Heads	Heads-up pennies	Tails-up pennies
Start	50	0
First toss		
Second toss		
Third toss		

2 **Using your model**

a. Make a graph showing the number of heads-up pennies on the *y*-axis and the number of tosses on the *x*-axis (0, 1, 2, 3, etc.).

b. On average, what percentage of pennies are lost (because they came up tails and were set aside) on each toss?

c. How does the concept of half-life relate to the experiment with pennies? What does one half-life correspond to?

3 **Build a radioactive atom**

Carbon - 14

8 neutrons

6 protons

6 electrons

1. Build a carbon-14 atom (C^{14}). This isotope of carbon is radioactive.
2. Take one neutron out, and replace it with one proton and one electron. This is what happens in radioactive decay of C^{14}.

4 **Constructing explanations**

a. Research what happens to C^{14} when it decays. What element does it become? What particles are given off?

b. What is the average time it takes for 50 percent of the C^{14} atoms in a sample to decay?

c. Suppose you watch 50 atoms of C^{14} for a very long time. How do the results of your penny-flipping experiment describe the number of C^{14} atoms?

d. We actually find C^{14} in the environment. Research where it comes from.

e. Describe two other types of radioactivity, and give an example of each.

f. *Challenge*: You cannot predict when any one atom will decay, just as you cannot predict whether a penny will come up heads or tails. Why can you predict that 50 percent of the C^{14} atoms in a sample will decay every half-life?

5   Introduction to Nuclear Reactions

If you were to add one, two, or four extra neutrons to lithium-7, you would have created lithium-8, lithium-9, and lithium-11, respectively. Each of these isotopes of lithium is *radioactive*. This means that the atomic force in the nucleus (called *strong nuclear force*) is not strong enough to hold these atoms together. The nuclei of these atoms fly apart.

The goal of Nuclear Reactions is to earn points by creating atoms that are stable (not radioactive) and neutrally charged (not ions). Remember that *ions* are atoms that have different numbers of protons and electrons so they have a charge.

Each player starts with eight protons, eight electrons, and eught neutrons in their pocket of the Atomic Building Game board. The game will last for about a half-hour. The first player with 20 points wins.

6   Playing Nuclear Reactions

To begin play, deal five cards from the deck of Nuclear Reactions cards to each player. These are held and not shown to anyone else.

Players take turns, choosing which card to play each turn and adding or subtracting particles from the atom as instructed on the card. For example, playing an Add 2 Electrons card would mean you place two yellow marbles in the atom.

Subatomic particles that you add or subtract from the atom must come from, or be placed in, your own pocket.

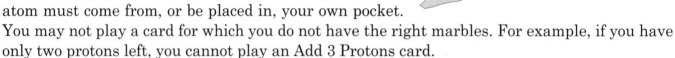

You may not play a card for which you do not have the right marbles. For example, if you have only two protons left, you cannot play an Add 3 Protons card.

Each time you play a card, draw a new card from the deck so you always have five cards. Played cards can be shuffled and reused as needed.

7 Scoring points

The number of points scored depends how many of the conditions below are satisfied by the atom you create. You can use the periodic table to determine strategy and points. In particular, it is useful to know which cards to play to get to stable isotopes, neutral atoms, or stable and neutral atoms.

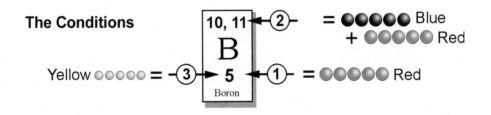

The Conditions

Condition 1: The number of protons (red or green marbles) matches the atomic number.
Condition 2: The number of protons (red or green marbles) plus the number of neutrons (blue marbles) equals one of the correct mass numbers for the element of condition 1. This creates a stable nucleus.
Condition 3: The number of electrons (yellow marbles) equals the number of protons (red or green marbles). This creates a neutral atom.

1. You score 1 point if your move creates or leaves a stable nucleus. For example, you score 1 point by adding a neutron to a nucleus with six protons and five neutrons. Adding a neutron makes a carbon-12 nucleus, which is stable. The next player can also score a point by adding another neutron, making carbon-13. Points cannot be scored for making a stable nucleus by adding or subtracting electrons because electrons are not found in the nucleus. To get the nucleus right, you need to satisfy conditions 1 and 2.

2. You score 1 point for adding or subtracting electrons or protons from the atom if your move creates or leaves a neutral atom. A neutral atom has the same number of electrons and protons. Getting the electrons and protons to balance satisfies condition 3.

3. You score 3 points (the best move) when you add or subtract particles from the atom and your move creates a perfect, stable, and neutral atom, meeting all three conditions. Both adding and subtracting can leave stable, neutral atoms. For example, taking a neutron from a stable, neutral carbon-13 atom leaves a stable, neutral carbon-12 atom, scoring 3 points.

8 Miscellaneous rules

Taking a turn

When it is your turn you must either

1. play a card and add or subtract marbles from the atom, or
2. trade in your cards for a new set of five.

Trading in cards

You may trade in all your cards at any time by forfeiting a turn. You have to trade all your cards in at once. Shuffle the deck before taking new cards.

Using the periodic table

All players should be allowed to use the special periodic table of the elements in the course of the game.

The marble bank

You may choose between two versions of the marble bank.

> **Version 1:** Players may take marbles from the bank at any time so they have enough to play the game.
>
> **Version 2:** Players must lose a turn to draw marbles from the bank, and may draw no more than five total marbles (of any colors) in one turn.

9 Arguing from evidence

Nuclear Fusion

$H^2 + H^2 \rightarrow He^4 + energy$

Nuclear Fission

$U^{235} \rightarrow Xe^{139} + Sr^{95} + n + energy$

a. There are two basic kinds of nuclear reactions, fission and fusion. Fission splits heavy elements into lighter elements. Fusion combines lighter elements to make heavier elements. Both fission and fusion can release energy, depending on which elements are involved. What element do you get when you fuse lithium-6 and boron-11 together? Is it stable or radioactive?

b. Write a nuclear reaction using only two elements that would allow you to build fluorine-19 starting with boron-10.

c. Suppose you split a uranium-238 atom. If you have to break it into two elements, name two that could be formed. Be sure that your two elements use up all the neutrons and protons in the uranium. Is either of your two elements stable? Is one (or are both) radioactive?

19C Solubility of CO$_2$

How is the solubility of a gas affected by temperature?

The carbonation in a soft drink is carbon dioxide gas that is dissolved in solution. The can is pressurized with carbon dioxide gas in order to maximize the amount of the gas dissolved in the beverage. As you have probably experienced, once you open the can, the carbon dioxide begins to escape and eventually the soda will taste "flat." The purpose of this investigation is to examine the solubility of carbon dioxide gas in solution.

Materials
- CPO DataCollector with temperature probe
- 2 Cans of carbonated soft drink
- 600-mL Beaker
- Thermometer
- Centigram balance
- Paper towels
- Heat-resistant gloves or hot mitts
- Hot plate

1 Making predictions

Based on what you know about carbonated drinks, how will the mass of carbon dioxide dissolved in solution change over time? When heated?

2 Doing the investigation

Part A: Solubility of carbon dioxide vs. time

1. Dry the outside of a room-temperature, unopened soft drink can.
2. Carefully open the can, and place it on the balance immediately. Record the mass in Table 1.
3. Record the mass every 3 minutes until 15 minutes have elapsed.
4. Don't discard the drink. Your teacher may have you record the mass one more time just before the period ends, so be sure to note the time you first opened the soda.

Part B: Temperature vs. solubility

1. Using a 600-milliliter beaker, measure out approximately 150 milliliters of water. Place a thermometer in the beaker.
2. Place the beaker on a hot plate, and heat it until the temperature is 55–60°C. Maintain this water temperature throughout the experiment.
3. Once the temperature of the water bath is reached, open the can and quickly measure its mass. Record the value in Table 2.
4. Use the temperature probe and DataCollector to measure the temperature of the beverage. Record the temperature in Table 2.
5. Carefully lower the opened can into the warm water. Place the temperature probe into the can, and select a new experiment on the DataCollector. Use the DataCollector in meter mode. When the temperature reaches 25°C, remove the can, dry it, and measure its mass. Record the value in Table 2.

203

6. Repeat step 5 after every 5°C increase until the temperature of the beverage reaches 50°C.

Table 1: Time and mass data

Time (min)	Mass (g)
0	
3	
6	
9	
12	
15	

Table 2: Temperature and mass data

Temperature (°C)	Mass (g)
Starting temp:	
25	
30	
35	
40	
45	
50	

3 Data analysis

a. Make a graph of the data in Table 1. Place time on the *x*-axis. Draw a best-fit straight line through the data if the relationship looks linear.

b. Make a graph of the data in Table 2. Place temperature on the *x*-axis.

4 Constructing explanations

a. What does the first graph show?

b. Examine the data in Table 2. What effect did a rise in temperature have on the mass of carbonated beverage in the opened can? Explain this result.

c. What does your second graph indicate about the relationship between temperature and the solubility of a gas (carbon dioxide)?

d. In the summertime, there is a risk that large populations of freshwater fish may die. Apply what you have observed in this investigation to explain this phenomenon.

204

20C Electric Charge

What is static electricity?

Have you ever felt a shock when you touched a metal doorknob or removed clothes from a dryer? A tiny imbalance in either positive or negative charge on an object can produce *static electricity*. In this investigation, you will cause objects to have charge imbalances and then observe what happens when different objects interact. Remember, positive and negative charges attract, while like charges repel.

Materials

- Clean glass beaker
- Plastic rod
- Aluminum foil
- Silk, fur, and/or fleece fabric
- Thread
- 18–22-gauge Copper wire
- Balloon
- Paper clip and pencil

1 Observing electric charge

Aluminum foil leaf

3-4 cm

Make two identical leaves.

Hang the leaf on some thread.

Rub a balloon against your hair and bring it near the leaf.

1. Cut out two small leaves of aluminum foil, and use a paper clip to make a hole in the top of each leaf. You can hold the leaf against a pencil as you poke the hole.
2. Suspend one leaf from a thread that you hold up in one hand.
3. Rub an inflated balloon against your hair, and move it toward the foil leaf.
4. Touch the rubbed part of the balloon to something metal, then bring it close to the leaf.
5. Bring other objects near the leaf before and after they are rubbed with different materials, such as silk, fleece, or fur.

2 Constructing explanations

a. Describe what happens to the aluminum foil leaf as you move the rubbed balloon closer.

b. Explain the reaction of the leaf to the balloon using the concepts of positive and negative charge.

c. Explain why touching the balloon to a metal object changed its effect on the leaf.

3 Making an electroscope

1. Cut a piece of insulated copper wire so it is about 10 centimeters long.

2. Strip about 2 centimeters of insulation from the wire at both ends. Be careful not to break the wire.

3. Bend the wire over the edge of the glass beaker as shown in the photo. It helps to place a small bit of clay on the rim to anchor the wire.

4. Make the electroscope as shown in the photo by hanging two foil leaves on the end of the wire that is inside the beaker.

5. Rub an inflated balloon against your hair, and move it toward the end of the wire sticking out of the beaker.

6. Touch the balloon to the wire, then remove it.

7. Touch the end of the wire with your finger or a metal object.

8. Bring the plastic rod near the wire. Then rub the plastic rod with the fleece, and bring it near the wire again.

Strip insulation from wire.

Hang leaves on a shallow hook so they are free to swing.

4 Constructing explanations

a. Describe what happens to the aluminum foil leaves as you move the rubbed balloon closer.

b. Give a reason why the leaves stay apart after the balloon is removed.

c. Explain what happens when you touch the wire with your finger or a metal object.

d. "Charge" the electroscope by touching it with a balloon that has been rubbed against your hair. Then touch the rubbed side of the balloon to something metal, and bring it close to the electroscope again. Describe what happens.

e. Why does the plastic rod cause the leaves to move only after it has been rubbed with the fleece?

f. What causes the leaves of the electroscope to move apart?

21C Analyzing Circuits

How do you build and analyze a network circuit?

When both series and parallel circuits are combined into one circuit, a *network circuit* is created. In this investigation, you will build and analyze network circuits. After determining the resistance of the colored resistors in the Electric Circuits kit, you will use these to build your network circuits.

Materials

*   CPO Electric Circuits kit
*   5-, 10-, and 20-ohm Resistors (in kit)
*   Tape and a marker for labeling
*   Digital multimeter with leads
*   2 D batteries

1 Determining the resistance of each resistor

You will use three different-colored resistors in this investigation. Use tape to label the green resistors R1 and R2, the blue resistor R3, and the red resistor R4.

Use the multimeter to measure the resistance in ohms (Ω) of each resistor. Enter the results in Table 1.

Measuring resistance

Ohms (Ω)

Table 1: Measured resistance values

	R1 (green)	R2 (green)	R3 (blue)	R4 (red)
Resistance (Ω)				

2 Building a network circuit

1. Use a battery; resistors 1, 2, and 3; and as many wires as necessary to construct the network circuit shown in the diagram at right.

2. Measure the voltage across the battery. This is the total circuit voltage. Then measure the voltage across each of the resistors. Record your measurements in Table 2.

3. Measure the current through each resistor. Record your measurements in Table 2. You have to break the circuit temporarily to insert the meter and make each current measurement. Be sure the meter is set to DC amps.

Build this circuit.

3 | Analyzing the circuit

	Battery (total circuit)	R1	R2	R3
Voltage (V)				
Current (A)				

a. Which resistors are connected in parallel?

b. Which resistor is in series with the other two?

c. How does the voltage across the parallel resistors compare?

d. How does the voltage across the parallel resistors relate to what you learned about voltages in a parallel circuit in a previous investigation?

e. How does the current flowing through R_1 compare with the current through R_2?

f. How does the current coming out of the battery compare with the sum of the currents flowing through R_2 and R_3? Explain this relationship.

g. Use what you know about series and parallel circuits to calculate the theoretical total resistance of the circuit. The formulas for finding the total resistance are

Series circuit	Parallel circuit
$R_{tot} = R_1 + R_2$	$\dfrac{1}{R_{tot}} = \dfrac{1}{R_1} + \dfrac{1}{R_2}$

h. Now calculate the total resistance of the circuit using Ohm's law, the battery voltage, and the total circuit current you measured.

i. How does the total resistance calculated using Ohm's law compare with the theoretical total resistance found above?

4 | Predicting the effect of changing a resistor

a. Replace the 10-ohm resistor (R_3) with the 20-ohm resistor (R_4). Use what you have learned about network circuits to predict the total circuit resistance and total circuit current. Show the process you used to make your predictions.

b. Measure the voltage across the battery and each resistor and the total current in the circuit. Use Ohm's law to find the total circuit resistance. You will need to make a data table similar to Table 2.

c. How did your predicted values compare with your measured ones? Calculate the percent error for the resistance.

5 A circuit puzzle

Build this circuit.

1. Build the circuit shown in the diagram above with two batteries, a switch, and three bulbs.
2. Observe the brightness of each bulb when you turn the switch on.
3. Temporarily interrupt the current to bulb B by disconnecting one wire from the terminal post.
4. Observe how the brightness of the other two bulbs changes.

a. When bulb B is disconnected, does bulb A get dimmer, brighter, or stay the same?

b. When bulb B is disconnected, does bulb C get dimmer, brighter, or stay the same?

c. Use what you know about series and parallel circuits to explain what you observed.

6 Challenge: Analyze a four-resistor network circuit

a. Build the circuit shown in the diagram at right.

b. Use what you have learned about network circuits to predict the total circuit resistance and current. Show the process you used to make your predictions.

c. Use the meter to measure the voltage across the battery and each resistor and the total circuit current. Use Ohm's law to find the total circuit resistance.

d. How did your predicted values compare with your measured ones? Calculate the percent error for the current and resistance.

22C Electromagnetic Forces

How does an electric motor work?

Electric motors are found in many household devices, such as hair dryers, blenders, drills, and fans. In this investigation, you will build a simple electric motor and see how it works. The concepts you learn with this simple motor also apply to other electric motors.

Materials

- Permanent magnet (from kit)
- D battery
- Large rubber band
- Metric ruler
- 1/2 stick of modeling clay
- Sandpaper
- Varnished magnet wire
- Paper clips
- CPO Timer II (optional)

1 Making the base

1. Bend the two paper clips so they look like the ones in the photo.
2. Fasten them with rubber bands so they contact the positive and negative terminals of the battery.
3. Break off a small lump of clay and set the battery on it so it stays in one place without rolling around.
4. Use a tiny piece of clay to stick a magnet to the top of the battery.
5. Your motor base is complete!

2 Making the coil

Sand all around this end of the wire.

Sand only one side of this end of the wire.

Coil

1. Cut 1 meter of magnet wire (also called varnished magnet wire). This wire has a painted insulation layer on the surface.
2. Wrap the wire around the square form of the modeling clay with one end sticking out about 4 centimeters.
3. Keep wrapping until you have only 4–5 centimeters left.
4. Remove your coil from the form, and wrap the ends of the wire a few turns around the sides of the coil to keep it together. There should be about 3 centimeters of wire on each side of the coil (see photo above).
5. Use sandpaper to sand off all the varnish on one end of the wire.
6. Sand off the varnish on *one side only* of the other end of the wire.
7. Adjust the wires until the coil balances as well as you can get it.
8. Your coil is done!

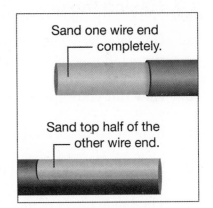

Sand one wire end completely.

Sand top half of the other wire end.

3 Making the motor work

1. Set the coil into the paper clip notches so it is free to spin.
2. Adjust the height of the paper clips until the coil rotates just above the magnet.
3. The motor should spin! Adjust the balance by bending the wires or paper clips.

Complete motor

Troubleshooting—the main problem areas to watch out for are

- unbalanced coil
- poor connections
- improperly sanded coil ends
- dead battery

211

4 Constructing explanations

a. When electricity runs through the coil of wire, what type of force is created around the coil?

b. What is the purpose of the permanent magnet?

c. What interactions cause the coil to spin?

d. Try adding a second magnet. Does this make the motor spin faster, slower, or at about the same speed? What observations did you make that support your answer?

e. What else might make the motor spin faster? With your teacher's approval, try it!

5 Planning and carrying out investigations

See if you can hold a photogate so the spinning coil breaks the light beam. Set the timer mode on frequency to measure how many breaks per second the spinning coil makes.

a. Describe how you set up the investigation to get frequency readings from the timer/photogate equipment.

b. How did your spinning coil measurements compare to other groups' data?

c. Repeat steps 4d and 4e with the timer/photogate setup. Record your data.

d. Does the spinning coil data support your answers to 4d and 4e? Explain.

e. The basic parts of any simple DC motor like the one you made are an electromagnet, a permanent magnet, a commutator, and an energy source. Draw a diagram of your simple motor, and label these parts.

23C Waves in Motion

How do waves move?

Waves are oscillations that move from one place to another. Like other oscillations, waves have the properties of frequency and amplitude. In this investigation, you will explore waves on springs and in water. What you learn applies to all other types of waves as well.

Materials

- Metal spring toy
- Meter stick
- 1-inch Length of plastic pipe cut to fit the wave tray
- Food coloring
- Water
- Wave tray with wooden blocks

1 Making a transverse wave pulse

Wave pulse

1. It takes two students to do this experiment. Each student takes one end of the spring.
2. Bring the spring down to the floor. Stretch it along the floor to a length of about 3 meters.
3. One student should jerk one end of the spring rapidly to the side and back, just once. Make sure both ends of the spring are held tight and do not move once the wave is in motion. A wave pulse should travel along the spring.
4. Watch the wave pulse as it moves out and back. Try it a few times.

2 Constructing explanations

a. How is the motion of a wave pulse different from the motion of a moving object such as a car? (*Hint*: What is it that moves in a wave?)

b. What happens to the wave pulse when it hits the far end of the spring? Watch carefully. Does the pulse stay on the same side of the spring or flip to the other side? Use the word *reflect* in your answer.

c. Suppose you broke the spring in the middle. Do you think the wave could cross the break? Explain why you think so.

d. Why does the wave pulse move along the spring instead of just staying in the place where you made it?

3 Making a longitudinal wave pulse

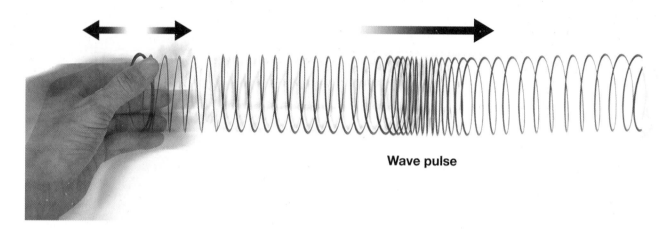

Wave pulse

1. As in Part 1, this experiment takes two students. Each student takes one end of the spring.

2. Bring the spring down to the floor. Stretch it along the floor to a length of about 3 meters.

3. One student should jerk one end of the spring rapidly forward and back, just once. Make sure both ends of the spring are held tight and do not move once the wave is in motion. A wave pulse should travel along the spring.

4. Watch the wave pulse as it moves out and back. Try it a few times.

4 Constructing explanations

a. How is the motion of the longitudinal wave pulse different from the transverse wave pulse you made in Part 1? (*Hint*: How is the motion of the spring itself different?)

b. What happens to the wave pulse when it hits the far end of the spring? Does it behave like the transverse wave or differently? Use the word *reflect* in your answer.

c. Why do you think longitudinal waves are sometimes called compressional waves?

d. Do you think a wave can be made by stretching the spring instead of compressing it? Make a prediction, then try it to see if you are right.

5 Waves in water

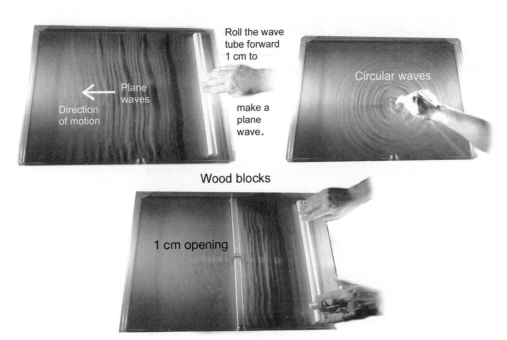

1. Fill a flat tray with about 0.5 centimeters of colored water. The color helps you see the waves.

2. Roll the wave tube forward about 1 centimeter in a smooth motion. This launches a nearly straight wave called a *plane wave* across the tray.

3. Next, poke the surface of the water with your fingertip. Disturbing a single point on the surface of the water makes a *circular wave* that moves outward from where you touched the water.

4. Arrange two wood blocks so they cross the tray leaving a 1-centimeter opening in the middle.

5. Make a plane wave that moves toward the blocks. Observe what happens to the wave that goes through the opening.

6 Constructing explanations

a. Draw a sketch showing your plane wave from above. Include an arrow indicating the direction the wave moves.

b. Is the plane wave parallel or perpendicular to the direction in which the wave moves?

c. Draw another sketch showing your circular wave. Add at least four arrows indicating the direction in which each part of the wave moves.

d. At every point along the wave, are the circular waves more parallel or perpendicular to the direction in which the waves move?

e. Sketch the shape of the wave before and after it passes through the narrow opening.

f. Does the wave change shape when it passes through the opening? If so, describe what you observe.

g. Are the waves you made in the water transverse or longitudinal waves? Why?

215

24C Perceiving Sound

What is sound, and how do we hear it?

The ear is a remarkable sensor. Sound waves that we can hear change the air pressure by as little as one part per million! Because sound is about perception and people's perceptions are different, we will have to use some very interesting techniques to conduct reliable experiments. In this investigation, you will learn about the range of frequencies the ear can detect and about how small a difference in frequency we can perceive.

Materials

- CPO DataCollector
- CPO Sound & Waves Machine
- Pencils
- Graph paper
- At least 1 calculator
- Ruler or straightedge

1 How high can you hear?

The accepted range of frequencies the human ear can hear ranges from a low of 20 Hz to a high of 20,000 Hz. Actually, there is tremendous variation within this range, and people's hearing changes greatly with age and exposure to loud noises.

Connect your sound generator to a DataCollector set to measure *frequency*. Connect a speaker to the sound generator. When you turn the DataCollector on, you should hear a sound, and the DataCollector should measure a frequency near 440 Hz.

There are two knobs: one for frequency and one for volume control. Try adjusting the frequency and seeing how high and low it will go.

As a group, agree on a frequency where you hear the sound as low, medium, high, and very high frequency. Write frequencies of sound that you think sound low, medium, high, and very high in Table 1. Don't try to be too exact because the words *low*, *medium*, and *high* are themselves not well defined. It is difficult to agree exactly on something based completely on individual human perception.

Table I: How we hear frequencies of sound

Description	Frequency (Hz)
Low	
Medium	
High	
Very high	

2 Testing the upper frequency limit of the ear

Start with a simple experiment. Your teacher has a sound generator that can make frequencies up to 20,000 Hz. When the teacher asks, raise your hand if you can hear the sound. Don't raise your hand if you can't hear it. Pick someone to count hands and see what fraction of students can still hear the sound as frequency increases.

a. The objective of the test is to see what fraction of people can hear a particular frequency. Once the frequency gets too high, no one will be able to hear it, or at least no humans. Cats, dogs, and other animals can hear much higher frequencies than people. Do you think the method of raising your hands is likely to give a good result? Give at least one reason why you think the method is reliable or not.

b. Make a bar graph showing how your class responded to frequencies between 10,000 and 20,000 Hz. You should have six bars, each one for a frequency range of 2,000 Hz. The height of each bar is the number of people who could hear that frequency of sound. If someone could hear the frequency, he or she is counted as a positive response in the graph. This kind of graph is called a *histogram*.

3 Doing a more careful experiment

Another way to do the experiment is with a secret ballot. The researcher running the experiment will ask who can hear a certain frequency of sound, and each participant will check yes or no on a survey sheet. The researcher may or may *not* play a sound. Each frequency will be played five times, with the five repetitions shuffled so there is less chance for error. Everyone in the class completes one survey sheet.

Survey		
#	Yes	No
1	✓	
2		✓
3		✓
4	✓	
5	✓	
6		✓
7	✓	
8		✓
9	✓	
10	✓	
11		

Key		Played	
#	Frequency	Yes	No
1	12,000	✓	
2	16,000		✓
3	10,000		✓
4	12,000	✓	
5	14,000	✓	
6	14,000		✓
7	18,000	✓	
8	20,000		✓
9	10,000	✓	
10	20,000	✓	
11	16,0		

Collect the data from the survey sheets, and record it in Table 2.

Table 2: Frequency survey data

# Right	10,000 Hz	12,000 Hz	14,000 Hz	16,000 Hz	18,000 Hz	20,000 Hz
5						
4						
3						
2						
1						

Plot another histogram showing only those people whose choices matched the yes/no on the key for all five times at each frequency. It is hard to fake a response or get it right by chance because you have to choose correctly five times for each frequency. This kind of experiment is called a double-blind test since neither you nor the researcher can see anyone else's responses. The results from a double-blind experiment are much more reliable than other forms of surveys. Doctors use the double-blind method to test new medicines.

4 Perceiving differences in frequency

Can you tell the difference between a sound with a frequency of 400 Hz and a sound at 401 Hz? The next hearing experiment tests people's ability to distinguish which of two sounds has the higher frequency.

The researcher will play two frequencies, A and B, and you mark which one is higher.

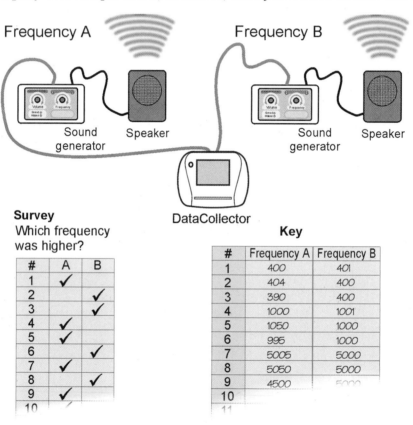

To analyze the results, you need to know how many people got the right answer for each frequency range. Make a data table like Table 3 that is large enough to hold all of your results.

Table 3: Comparative frequency data

Frequency A (Hz)	Frequency B (Hz)	Frequency difference (Hz)	Percent difference	# of correct responses
1,000	995	5	0.5%	1
1,000	1,050	50	1%	15
1,000	1,001	1	.1%	0

a. Calculate the percent difference in frequency for each test.

b. There are two ways to look at sensitivity. In one way, we hear *absolute* differences in frequency. If the ear was sensitive to absolute differences, we would hear a 5 Hz difference no matter if the two frequencies were 500 Hz and 505 Hz, or 5,000 Hz and 5,005 Hz.

In the other way, we hear *relative* differences. We might be able to hear a 1 percent difference at 500 Hz (which would be 5 Hz), but we could not hear the difference between 5,000 Hz and 5,005 Hz because the percentage difference is only 0.1 percent. To hear a similar difference at 5000 Hz, Frequency B would have to be 5,050 Hz, or 1 percent higher.

Which model, absolute or relative differences, does the data support?

5 **Chance and experiments**

A very good way to ensure accurate results in a survey test is to make it improbable that anyone could get the correct response by guessing. A single test is almost never enough to rule out this possibility. Consider that on each test you have a 50 percent chance to guess right. That means one out of every two times you could get the right response just by guessing. This is not very reliable!

The advantage of doing multiple trials

The diagram shows a decision tree for an experiment with multiple trials. There is only one path with no mistakes. With each additional trial, the total number of possible outcomes increases twofold. With two trials, you have one right path out of four choices. That means there is only a one in four chance someone could guess twice correctly. With three trials, there is only a one in eight chance of guessing correctly. With four trials, the chance of guessing correctly is down to 1 in 16.

a. What is the chance of guessing correctly with five trials?

b. If 100 people did a test with five trials and everybody just guessed, how many people would be likely to make five correct choices in a row?

25C Magnification and Mixing Pigments

How is the magnification of a lens determined? What happens when you mix different colors of pigments?

Lenses are optical devices that use refraction to bend light. Some lenses produce images that are larger than the object they are collecting light from. This process, called magnification, is used in equipment like microscopes and telescopes to investigate objects that are difficult to see with the naked eye. In this investigation, you will look at how distance can affect magnification. You will also explore how mixing materials colored by pigments, paints, or dyes is different from mixing different colors of light.

Materials

- CPO Optics with Light & Color kit
- Metric ruler
- Cyan, magenta, and yellow bakelite clay

1 Finding the magnification of a lens

1. Set your light blue lens directly on the graph paper, and count the number of *unmagnified* squares that cross the diameter of the lens. In the example, the lens is 10 squares wide.

2. Next, examine a section of graph paper with your lens held above the paper. Move the lens closer and farther away until you have the biggest squares you can still see clearly in the lens.

3. Count the number of *magnified* squares that cross the diameter of the lens. For example, the picture shows 4 1/2 squares across the lens.

4. The magnification can be calculated by dividing the number of *unmagnified* squares by the number of *magnified* squares. In the example, you see 10 *unmagnified* squares and 4.5 *magnified* squares. The magnification is 10 /4.5, or 2.22.

5. Try the experiment again, this time holding the lens above the paper and using a ruler to measure the distance between the lens and the paper. Notice that the magnification changes with different distances.

Measuring the distance from the lens to the paper

6. Fill in Table 1 by measuring the magnification of your lens for at least four different distances. The number of unmagnified squares on the graph paper will be the same for all distances.

Table 1: Magnification of a lens

Distance to paper	# of squares on graph paper (unmagnified squares)	# of squares in lens (magnified squares)	Magnification

2 Constructing explanations

a. Is the image in a magnifying glass inverted or upright?

b. At what distances does the lens act like a magnifying glass? What happens when the object is more than one focal length away?

c. Describe something that looks completely different under a magnifying glass than when seen with the unaided eye.

d. Try the same activity with the dark blue lens. What happens to the image in the lens when you lift the lens off the paper?

3 The subtractive color model (CMYK)

1. You have three colors of clay: cyan, magenta, and yellow. Mix equal portions (about the size of your fingertip) of the cyan and the magenta. What color do you get?

2. Mix equal amounts of cyan and yellow. What color do you get?

3. Mix equal amounts of yellow and magenta. What color do you get?

The subtractive color model (CMYK)

	Cyan	Magenta	Yellow	Black
Absorbs	Red	Green	Blue	Red, Green, Blue
Reflects	Blue, Green	Blue, Red	Red, Green	None

Cyan Magenta Yellow

Mix equal amounts of the three subtractive primary colors *(two colors at a time)*.

4 Constructing explanations

a. Explain how the mixture of magenta and cyan makes its color when seen in white light.

b. Explain how the mixture of cyan and yellow makes its color when seen in white light.

c. Explain how the mixture of yellow and magenta makes its color when seen in white light.

d. Why don't the mixed colors produce full red, green, or blue?

e. What color would you see if you looked at a mixture of magenta and cyan under a lamp that only made blue light?

f. Research how printers make colors. Do they use red, green, and blue (RGB) or cyan, magenta, yellow, and black (CMYK)? Explain why printed pictures need to use this method.

g. Research how computers and televisions make colors. Do they use red, green, and blue (RGB) or cyan, magenta, yellow, and black (CMYK)? Explain why these devices need to use this method.

h. Explain why mixing the primary colors of light is referred to as the additive color mixing process, while mixing materials colored with pigments, paints, or dyes is referred to as the subtractive color mixing process.

Lab Skills and Engineering Design Log

Safety Skills

What can I do to protect myself and others in the lab?

Science equipment and supplies are fun to use. However, these materials must always be used with care. Here you will learn how to be safe in a science lab.

Materials

- Poster board
- Felt-tip markers

 Follow these basic safety guidelines

Your teacher will divide the class into groups. Each group should create a poster-sized display of one of the following guidelines. Hang the posters in the lab. Review these safety guidelines before each investigation.

1. **Prepare** for each investigation.

   a. Read the investigation sheets carefully.

   b. Take special note of safety instructions.

2. **Listen** to your teacher's instructions before, during, and after the investigation. Take notes to help you remember what your teacher has said.

3. **Get ready to work:** Roll long sleeves above the wrist. Tie back long hair. Remove dangling jewelry and any loose, bulky outer layers of clothing. Wear shoes that cover the toes.

4. **Gather protective clothing** (goggles, apron, gloves) at the beginning of the investigation.

5. **Emphasize teamwork.** Help each other. Watch out for one another's safety.

6. **Clean up** spills immediately. Clean up all materials and supplies after an investigation.

 Know what to do when...

1. **working with heat.**

   a. Always handle hot items with a hot pad. Never use your bare hands.

   b. Move carefully when you are near hot items. Sudden movements could cause burns if you touch or spill something hot.

2. **working with electricity.**

   a. Always keep electric cords away from water.

   b. Extension cords must not be placed where they may cause someone to trip or fall.

   c. If an electrical appliance isn't working, feels hot, or smells hot, tell a teacher right away.

3. **disposing of materials and supplies.**

    a. Generally, liquid household chemicals can be poured into a sink. Completely wash the chemical down the drain with plenty of water.

    b. Generally, solid household chemicals can be placed in a trash can.

    c. Any liquids or solids that **should not** be poured down the sink or placed in the trash have special disposal guidelines. Follow your teacher's instructions.

    d. If glass breaks, do not use your bare hands to pick up the pieces. Use a dustpan and brush to clean up. "Sharps" trash (trash that has pieces of glass) should be well labeled. The best way to throw away broken glass is to seal it in a labeled cardboard box.

4. **you are concerned about your safety or the safety of others.**

    a. Talk to your teacher immediately. Here are some examples:

        • You smell chemical or gas fumes. This might indicate a chemical or gas leak.

        • You smell something burning.

        • You injure yourself or see someone else who is injured.

        • You are having trouble using your equipment.

        • You do not understand the instructions for the investigation.

    b. Listen carefully to your teacher's instructions.

    c. Follow your teacher's instructions exactly.

3 Safety quiz

1. Draw a diagram of your science lab in the space below. Include in your diagram the following items, along with notes that explain how to use them.

- Exit/entrance ways
- Eye wash and shower
- Sink
- Fire extinguisher(s)
- First aid kit
- Trash cans
- Fire blanket
- Location of eye goggles and lab aprons
- Location of special safety instructions

2. How many fire extinguishers are in your science lab? Explain how to use them.

_____

_____

3. List the steps that your teacher and your class would take to safely exit the science lab and the building in case of a fire or other emergency.

_____

_____

_____

_____

4. Before beginning certain investigations, why should you first put on protective goggles and clothing?

_____

_____

_____

5. Why is teamwork important when you are working in a science lab?

_____

_____

_____

_____

6. Why should you clean up after every investigation?

_____

_____

_____

7. List at least three things you should you do if you sense danger or see an emergency in your classroom or lab.

_____

_____

_____

_____

8. Six lab situations are described below. What would you do in each situation?
   a. You accidentally knock over a glass container, and it breaks on the floor.

_____

_____

   b. You accidentally spill a large amount of water on the floor.

_____

_____

c. You suddenly you begin to smell a "chemical" odor that gives you a headache.

_____

_____

_____

d. You hear the fire alarm while you are working in the lab. You are wearing your goggles and lab apron.

_____

_____

_____

e. While your lab partner has her lab goggles off, she gets some liquid from the experiment in her eye.

_____

_____

_____

f. A fire starts in the lab.

_____

_____

_____

Safety in the science lab is everyone's responsibility!

Safety contract

Keep this contract in your notebook at all times.

By signing it, you agree to follow all the steps necessary to be safe in your science class and lab.

I, _____ , (Your name)

· Have learned about the use and location of the following:
   · Aprons, gloves
   · Eye protection
   · Eyewash fountain
   · Fire extinguisher and fire blanket
   · First aid kit
   · Heat sources (burners, hot plate, etc.) and how to use them safely
   · Waste-disposal containers for glass, chemicals, matches, paper, and wood
· Understand the safety information presented.
· Will ask questions when I do not understand safety instructions.
· Pledge to follow all of the safety guidelines that are presented on the Safety Skills sheet at all times.
· Pledge to follow all of the safety guidelines that are presented on investigation sheets.
· Will always follow the safety instructions that my teacher provides.

Additionally, I pledge to be careful about my own safety and to help others be safe. I understand that I am responsible for helping to create a safe environment in the classroom and lab.

Signed and dated,

_____

Parent's or Guardian's statement:

I have read the Safety Skills sheet and give my consent for the student who has signed the preceding statement to engage in laboratory activities using a variety of equipment and materials, including those described. I pledge my cooperation in urging that she or he observe the safety regulations prescribed.

_____   _____
Signature of Parent or Guardian   Date

Writing a Lab Report

How do you share the results of an experiment?

A lab report is like a story about an experiment. The details in the story help others learn from what you did. A good lab report makes it possible for someone else to repeat your experiment. If their results and conclusions are similar to yours, you have support for your ideas. Through this process we come to understand more about how the world works.

 The parts of a lab report

A lab report follows the steps of the scientific method. Use the checklist below when you create your own lab reports.

☐ **Title:** The title makes it easy for readers to quickly identify the topic of your experiment.

☐ **Research question:** The research question tells the reader exactly what you want to find out through your experiment.

☐ **Introduction:** This paragraph describes what you already know about the topic and shows how this information relates to your experiment.

☐ **Hypothesis:** The hypothesis states the prediction you plan to test in your experiment.

☐ **Materials:** List all the materials and equipment you need in order to do the experiment.

☐ **Procedure:** Describe the steps involved in your experiment. Make sure that you provide enough detail so readers can repeat what you did. You may want to provide sketches of the lab setup. Be sure to name both the experimental variable and variables you controlled.

☐ **Data/Observations:** This is where you record what happened, using descriptive words, data tables, and graphs.

☐ **Analysis:** In this section, explain your data in words. Here's a good way to start: *My data shows that...*

☐ **Conclusion:** This paragraph states whether your hypothesis was correct or incorrect. It may suggest a new research question or a new hypothesis.

 A sample lab report

Use the sample lab report on the next two pages as a guide for writing your own lab reports. Remember that you are telling a story about something you did so that others can repeat your experiment.

Name: Lucy O.   **Date:** January 24, 2017

Title: Pressure and Speed

Research question: How does pressure affect the speed of the CPO air rocket?

Introduction:

Air pressure is a term used to describe how tightly air molecules are packed into a certain space. When air pressure increases, more air molecules are packed into the same amount of space. These molecules are moving around and colliding with each other and the walls of the container. As the number of molecules in the container increases, the number of molecular collisions in the container increases. A pressure gauge measures the force of these molecules as they strike a surface.

In this lab, I will measure the speed of the CPO air rocket when it is launched with different amounts of initial pressure inside the plastic bottle. I want to know if a greater amount of initial air pressure will cause the air rocket to travel at a greater speed.

Hypothesis: When I increase the pressure of the air rocket, the speed will increase.

Materials:

CPO air rocket   CPO photogates

CPO timer   Goggles

Procedure:

1. I put on goggles and made sure the area was clear.
2. The air rocket is attached to an arm so that it travels in a circular path. After it travels about 330°, the air rocket hits a stopper and its flight ends. I set up the photogate at 90°.
3. My control variables were the mass of the rocket and launch technique, so I kept these constant throughout the experiment.
4. My experimental variable was the initial pressure applied to the rocket. I tested the air rocket at three different initial pressures. The pressures that work effectively with this equipment range from 15 psi to 90 psi. I tested the air rocket at 20 psi, 50 psi, and 80 psi. I did three trials at each pressure.
5. The length of the rocket wing is 5 cm. The wing breaks the photogate's light beam. The photogate reports the amount of time that the wing took to pass through the beam. Therefore, I used wing length as distance and divided by time to calculate speed of the air rocket.
6. I found the average speed in centimeters per second for each pressure.

Data/Observations:

Table 1:Air pressure and speed of rocket

Initial air pressure	Time (s) at 90°	Speed (m/s) at 90°	Average speed (cm/s)
20 psi	0.0227	2.20	216
	0.0231	2.16	
	0.0237	2.11	
50 psi	0.0097	5.15	510
	0.0099	5.05	
	0.0098	5.10	
80 psi	0.0060	8.33	794
	0.0064	7.81	
	0.0065	7.69	

Speed vs. pressure

Analysis:

My graph shows that the plots of the data for photogates A and B are linear. As the values for pressure increased, the speed increased also.

Conclusion:

The data shows that pressure does have an effect on speed. The graph shows that my hypothesis is correct. As the initial pressure of the rocket increased, the speed of the rocket increased as well. There is a direct relationship between pressure and speed of the rocket.

Measuring Length

How do you find the length of an object?

Size matters! When you describe the length of an object or the distance between two objects, you are describing something very important about the object. Is it as small as a bacteria (2 micrometers)? Is it a light year away (9.46×10^{15} meters)? By using the metric system, you can quickly see differences in size.

Materials

- Metric ruler
- Pencil
- Paper
- Small objects
- Calculator

 Reading the meter scale correctly

Look at the ruler in the picture above. Each short line on the top of the ruler represents one millimeter. Longer lines indicate 5-millimeter and 10-millimeter intervals. When the object you are measuring falls between the lines, read the number to the nearest 0.5 millimeter. Practice measuring several objects with your own metric ruler. Compare your results with a lab partner's.

2 **Analyzing and interpreting data**

a. You may have seen a ruler like this marked in centimeter units. How many millimeters are in 1 centimeter?

_____

_____

_____

b. Notice that the ruler also has markings for reading the English system. Give an example of when it would be better to measure with the English system than the metric system. Give a different example of when it would be better to use the metric system.

_____

_____

_____

Example 1: Measuring objects correctly

Look at the picture above. How long is the building block?

1. Report the length of the building block to the nearest 0.5 millimeter.
2. Convert your answer to centimeters.
3. Convert your answer to meters.

_____

_____

_____

_____

_____

_____

_____

_____

_____

_____

_____

_____

_____

Example 2: Measuring objects correctly

Look at the picture above. How long is the pencil?

1. Report the length of the pencil to the nearest 0.5 millimeter.
2. *Challenge*: How many building blocks in example 1 will it take to equal the length of the pencil?
3. *Challenge*: Convert the length of the pencil to inches by dividing your answer by 25.4 millimeters per inch.

 Example 3: Measuring objects correctly

Look at the picture above. How long is the domino?

1. Report the length of the domino to the nearest 0.5 millimeter.
2. *Challenge*: How many dominoes will fit end to end on the 30-centimeter ruler?

6 ▲ Practice converting units for length

By completing the examples above, you show that you are familiar with some of the prefixes used in the metric system, like milli- and centi-. The table below gives other prefixes you may be less familiar with. Convert the length of the domino from millimeters into all the other units in the table.

Refer to the multiplication factor this way:

- 1 kilometer equals 1,000 meters.

- 1,000 millimeters equals 1 meter.

1. How many millimeters are in a kilometer?

$$\frac{1,000 \text{ millimeters}}{1 \text{ meter}} \times \frac{1,000 \text{ meters}}{1 \text{ kilometer}} = \frac{1,000,000 \text{ mm}}{1 \text{ km}} = 1 \times 10^{6} \text{ mm/km}$$

2. Fill in the multiplication factor by converting millimeters to the unit given. The first one is done for you.

$$\frac{1,000 \text{ millimeters}}{1 \text{ meter}} \times \frac{1 \times 10^{-12} \text{ meters}}{1 \text{ picometer}} = 1 \times 10^{-9} \text{ mm/pm}$$

3. Divide the domino's length in millimeters by the number in the multiplication factor column. This is the answer you will put in the last column.

Prefix	Symbol	Multiplication factor	Scientific notation in meters	Multiplication factor	Domino length in:
pico-	p	0.000000000001	10^{-12}	10^{-9}	pm
nano-	n	0.000000001	10^{-9}		nm
micro-	μ	0.000001	10^{-6}		μm
milli-	m	0.001	10^{-3}		mm
centi-	c	0.01	10^{-2}		cm
deci-	d	0.1	10^{-1}		dm
deka-	da	10	10^{1}		dam
hecto-	h	100	10^{2}		hm
kilo-	k	1,000	10^{3}		km

Measuring Temperature

How do you find the temperature of a substance?

Many different kinds of thermometers are used to measure temperature. Can you think of some you use at home? In your classroom, you will use an immersion thermometer to find the temperature of a liquid. The thermometer contains alcohol with a red dye in it so you can see the alcohol level inside the thermometer. The alcohol level changes depending on the surrounding temperature. You will practice reading the scale on the thermometer and reporting your readings in degrees Celsius.

Materials

- Alcohol immersion thermometer
- Beakers
- Water at different temperatures
- Ice

Safety: Glass thermometers are breakable. Handle them carefully. Overheating the thermometer can cause the alcohol to separate and give incorrect readings. Glass thermometers should be stored horizontally or vertically (never upside down) to prevent alcohol from separating.

 Reading the temperature scale correctly

Look at the picture at the right. See the close-up of the temperature line and the scale. The tens scale numbers are given. The ones scale appears as lines. Each short line equals 1 degree Celsius (°C). Practice reading the scale from the bottom to the top. One short line above 20°C is read as 21°C. When the level of the alcohol is between two short lines on the scale, report the number to the nearest 0.5°C.

 Analyzing and interpreting data

a. What number does the longer line halfway between 20°C and 30°C equal? Figure out by counting the number of short lines between 20°C and 30°C.

b. Give the temperature shown on the thermometer.

c. Practice rounding the following temperature values to the nearest 0.5°C: 23.1°C, 29.8°C, 30.0°C, 31.6°C, 31.4°C.

d. Water at 0°C and 100°C has different properties. Describe what water looks like at these temperatures.

e. What will happen to the level of the alcohol if you hold the thermometer by the bulb?

Reading the temperature of water in a beaker

An immersion thermometer must be placed in liquid up to the solid line on the thermometer (at least 2 1/2 inches of liquid). Wait about 3 minutes for the temperature of the thermometer to equal the temperature of the liquid. When the level stops moving, record the temperature to the nearest 0.5°C.

1. Place the thermometer in the beaker. Check to make sure that the water level is above the solid line on the thermometer.

2. Wait until the alcohol level stops moving (about 3 minutes). Record the temperature to the nearest 0.5°C.

 ## Reading the temperature of warm water in a beaker

A warm liquid will cool to room temperature. For a warm liquid, record the warmest temperature you observe before the temperature begins to decrease.

1. Repeat the procedure in Part 3 with a beaker of warm (not boiling) water.

2. Take temperature readings every 30 seconds. Record the warmest temperature you observe.

 ## Reading the temperature of ice water in a beaker

When a large amount of ice is added to water, the temperature of the water will drop until the ice and water are the same temperature. After the ice has melted, the cold water will warm to room temperature.

1. Repeat the procedure in Part 3 with a beaker of ice and water.

2. Take temperature readings every 30 seconds. Record the coldest temperature you observe.

Calculating Volume

How do you find the volume of a three-dimensional shape?

Volume is the amount of space an object takes up. If you know the dimensions of a solid object, you can find the object's volume. A two-dimensional shape has length and width. A three-dimensional object has length, width, and height. This investigation gives you practice in finding volume for different solid objects.

Materials

- Pencil
- Calculator

 ## Calculating volume of a cube

A cube is a geometric solid that has length, width, and height. If you measure the sides of a cube, you will find that all the edges have the same measurement. The volume of a cube is found by multiplying the length times width times height. In the picture, each side measures 4 centimeters, so the problem looks like this:

$$V = l \times w \times h$$

Height = 4 cm

Width = 4 cm

Length = 4 cm

Example:

Volume = 4 centimeters × 4 centimeters × 4 centimeters = 64 centimeters^3

 ## Analyzing and interpreting data

a. What are the units for volume in the example above?

b. If the edge of a cube is 4 inches, what will the volume be? Give the units.

c. How is finding volume different from finding area?

d. If you had cubes with a length of 1 centimeter, how many would you need to build the cube in Part 1?

3 ◣ Calculating volume of a rectangular prism

Rectangular prisms are like cubes, except not all of the sides are equal. A shoebox is a rectangular prism. You can find the volume of a rectangular prism using the same formula as for a cube:
$V = l \times w \times h$.

Height = 2 cm
Width = 3 cm
Length = 8 cm

Another way to say it is to multiply the area of the base times the height.

1. Find the area of the base for the rectangular prism pictured here.

2. Multiply the area of the base times the height. Record the volume of the rectangular prism.

3. *Practice*: Find the volume for a rectangular prism with a height 6 cm, length 5 cm, and width 3 cm. Be sure to include the units in all of your answers.

4 ◣ Calculating volume for a triangular prism

Triangular prisms have three sides and two triangular bases. The volume of a triangular prism is found by multiplying the area of the base times the height. The base is a triangle.

Height = 6 cm
Base width = 2 cm
Base length = 3 cm

1. Find the area of the base by solving for the area of the triangle: $B = \frac{1}{2} \times l \times w$.

2. Find the volume by multiplying the area of the base times the height of the prism: $V = B \times h$. Record the volume of the triangular prism shown here.

3. *Practice*: Find the volume of a triangular prism with a height 10 cm, triangular base width 4 cm, and triangular base length 5 cm.

5 ◣ Calculating volume for a cylinder

A soup can is a cylinder. A cylinder has two circular bases and a round surface. The volume of a cylinder is found by multiplying the area of the base times the height. The base is a circle.

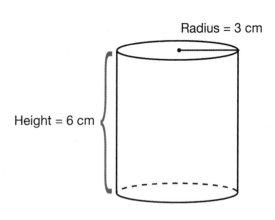

Radius = 3 cm
Height = 6 cm

1. Find the area of the base by solving for the area of a circle: $A = \pi \times r^2$.

2. Find the volume by multiplying the area of the base times the height of the cylinder: $V = A \times h$. Record the volume of the cylinder shown here.

3. *Practice*: Find the volume of the cylinder with height 8 cm and radius 4 cm.

240

6 ▲ Calculating volume for a cone

An ice cream cone really is a cone! A cone has height and a circular base. The volume of a cone is found by multiplying $1/2$ times the area of the base times the height.

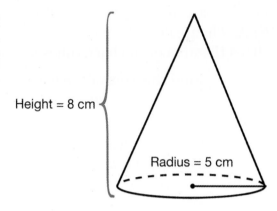

Height = 8 cm

Radius = 5 cm

1. Find the area of the base by solving for the area of a circle: $A = \pi \times r^2$.

2. Find the volume by multiplying $1/2$ times the area of the base times the height: $V = 1/2 \times A \times h$. Record the volume of the cone shown here.

3. *Practice*: Find the volume of the cone with height 8 cm and radius 4 cm. Contrast your answer with the volume you found for the cylinder with the same dimensions. What is the difference in volume? Does this make sense?

7 ▲ Calculating the volume for a rectangular pyramid

A pyramid looks like a cone. It has height and a rectangular base. The volume of a rectangular pyramid is found by multiplying $1/3$ times the area of the base times the height.

Height = 6 cm

Width = 4 cm

Length = 5 cm

1. Find the area of the base by multiplying the length times the width: $A = l \times w$.

2. Find the volume by multiplying $1/3$ times the area of the base times the height: $V = 1/3 \times A \times h$. Record the volume of the rectangular pyramid shown here.

3. *Practice*: Find the volume of a rectangular pyramid with height 10 cm, width 4 cm, and length 5 cm.

4. *Extra Challenge*: If a rectangular pyramid had a height of 8 cm and a width of 4 cm, what length would it need to have to give the same volume as the cone in practice question 3 above?

Calculating volume for a triangular pyramid

A triangular pyramid is like a rectangular pyramid, but its base is a triangle. Find the area of the base first. Then calculate the volume by multiplying $1/3$ times the area of the base times the height.

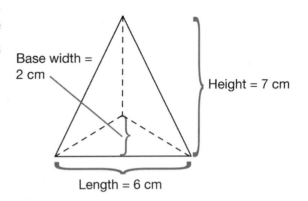

Base width = 2 cm

Height = 7 cm

Length = 6 cm

1. Find the area of the base by solving for the area of a triangle: $B = 1/2 \times l \times w$.

2. Find the volume by multiplying $1/3$ times the area of the base times the height: $V = 1/3 \times A \times h$. Find the volume of the triangular pyramid shown here.

3. *Practice*: Find the volume of a triangular pyramid with height 10 cm, width 6 cm, and length 5 cm.

 ## Calculating volume for a sphere

To find the volume of a sphere, you only need to know one dimension, its radius.

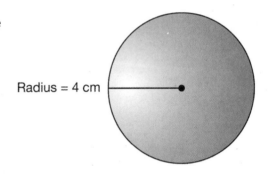

Radius = 4 cm

1. Find the volume of a sphere: $V = 4/3\pi r^3$. Find the volume for the sphere shown here.

2. *Practice*: Find the volume of a sphere with radius 2 cm.

3. *Extra Challenge*: Find the volume of a sphere with diameter 10 cm.

Measuring Volume

How do you find the volume of an irregular object?

It's easy to find the volume of a shoebox or a basketball. You just take a few measurements, plug the numbers into a math formula, and you have figured it out. But what if you want to find the volume of a bumpy rock, or an acorn, or a house key? There aren't any simple math formulas to help you out. However, there is an easy way to find the volume of an irregular object, as long the object is waterproof!

Materials

- Displacement tank
- Water source
- Disposable cup
- Beaker
- Graduated cylinder
- Sponges or paper towels
- Object to be measured

1 ◣ Setting up the displacement tank

Set the displacement tank on a level surface. Place a disposable cup under the spout. Carefully fill the tank until the water begins to drip out of the spout. When the water stops dripping, discard the water collected in the disposable cup. Set the cup aside, and place a beaker under the spout.

Displacement tank

Spout

Water line

Object to be measured

2 ◣ Analyzing and interpreting data

a. What do you think will happen when you place an object into the tank?

b. Which object would cause more water to come out of the spout, an acorn or a fist-sized rock?

c. Why are we interested in how much water comes out of the spout?

d. Explain how the displacement tank measures volume.

3 ◣ Measuring volume with the displacement tank

1. Gently place a waterproof object into the displacement tank. It is important to avoid splashing the water or creating a wave that causes extra water to flow out of the spout. It may take a little practice to master this step.

2. When the water stops flowing out of the spout, it can be poured from the beaker into a graduated cylinder for precise measurement. The volume of the water displaced is equal to the object's volume.
   Note: Occasionally, when a small object is placed in the tank, no water will flow out. This happens because an air bubble has formed in the spout. Simply tap the spout with a pencil to release the air bubble.

3. If you wish to measure the volume of another object, be sure to refill the tank first!

Measuring Mass with a Triple-Beam Balance

How do you find the mass of an object?

Why can't you use a bathroom scale to measure the mass of a paper clip? You could if you were finding the mass of a lot of them at one time! To find the mass of objects less than a kilogram, you need to use a triple-beam balance.

Materials

- Triple-beam balance
- Small objects
- Mass set (optional)
- Beaker

 Parts of the triple-beam balance

 Setting up and zeroing the balance

The triple-beam balance works like a see-saw. When the mass of your object is perfectly balanced by the counter masses on the beam, the pointer will rest at 0. Add up the readings on the three beams to find the mass of your object. The unit of measure for this triple-beam balance is grams.

1. Place the balance on a level surface.

2. Clean any objects or dust off the pan.

3. Move all counter masses to 0. The pointer should rest at 0. Use the adjustment screw to adjust the pointer to 0, if necessary. When the pointer rests at 0 with no objects on the pan, the balance is said to be zeroed.

Finding a known mass

You can check that the triple-beam balance is working correctly by using a mass set. Your teacher will provide the correct mass values for these objects.

1. After zeroing the balance, place an object with a known mass on the pan.

2. Move the counter masses to the right one at a time from largest to smallest. When the pointer is resting at 0, the numbers under the three counter masses should add up to the known mass.

3. If the pointer is above or below 0, recheck the balance setup. Recheck the position of the counter masses. Counter masses must be properly seated in a groove. Check with your teacher to make sure you are getting the correct mass before measuring the mass of an unknown object.

 Finding the mass of an unknown object

1. After zeroing the balance, place an object with an unknown mass on the pan. Do not place hot objects or chemicals directly on the pan.

2. Move the largest counter mass first. Place it in the first notch after 0. Wait until the pointer stops moving. If the pointer is above 0, move the counter mass to the next notch. Continue to move the counter mass to the right, one notch at a time, until the pointer is slightly above 0. Go to step 3. If the pointer is below 0, move the counter mass back one notch. When the pointer rests at 0, you do not need to move any more counter masses.

3. Move the next largest counter mass from 0 to the first notch. Watch to see where the pointer rests. If it rests above 0, move the counter mass to the next notch. Repeat until the point rests at 0, or slightly above. If the pointer is slightly above 0, go to step 4.

4. Move the smallest counter mass from 0 to the position on the beam where the pointer rests at 0.

5. Add the masses from the three beams to get the mass of the unknown object. You should be able to record a number for the hundreds place, the tens place, the ones place, the tenths place, and the hundredths place. The hundredths place can be read to 0.00 or 0.05. You may have zeros in your answer.

5 ◢ Reading the balance correctly

Look at the picture above. To find the mass of the object, locate the counter mass on each beam. Read the number directly below each counter mass. You can read the smallest mass to 0.05 grams. Write the three numbers and add them together. Report your answer in grams. Does your answer agree with others? If not, check your mass value from each beam to find your mistake.

6 ◢ Finding the mass of an object in a container

To measure the mass of a liquid or powder, you need an empty container on the pan to hold the sample. You must find the mass of the empty container first. After you place the sample in the container and find the total mass, subtract the massof the container to find the mass of the liquid or powder.

1. After zeroing the balance, place a beaker on the pan.

2. Follow directions for finding the mass of an unknown object. Record the mass of the beaker.

3. Place a small sample of liquid or powder in the beaker.

4. Move the counter masses to the right, largest to smallest, to find the total mass.

5. Subtract the beaker's mass from the total mass. This is the mass of your sample in grams.

Recording Observations in the Lab

How do you record valid observations for an experiment in the lab?

Whenever you conduct an experiment, you make important observations. You and others can then use these observations to test a hypothesis. In order for an experiment to be valid, the evidence you collect must be objective and repeatable. This investigation gives you practice making and recording valid, useful observations.

Materials

- Paper
- Pencil
- Calculator
- Ruler

 Making valid observations

Valid scientific observations are objective and repeatable. Scientific observations are made with one's senses and with tools and equipment. An objective observation means that the observer records only what happened, using data, words, and pictures to describe the observations as precisely as possible. An experiment is repeatable if other scientists can follow the procedure and get the same result. Exercise 1 gives you practice identifying good scientific observations.

 Exercise 1

1. **Which observation is the most objective? Circle the correct letter.**

    a. My frog died after 3 days in the aquarium. I miss him.

    b. The frog died after 3 days in the aquarium. We will test the temperature and water conditions to find out why.

    c. Frogs tend to die in captivity. Ours did after three days.

2. **Which observation is the most descriptive? Circle the correct letter.**

    a. After weighing 3.000 grams of sodium bicarbonate into an Erlenmeyer flask, we slowly added 50.0 milliliters of vinegar. The contents of the flask began to bubble.

    b. We weighed the powder into a glass container. We added acid. It bubbled a lot.

    c. We saw a fizzy reaction.

3. **Which experiment report has enough detail to repeat? Circle the correct letter.**

   a. Each student took a swab culture from his or her teeth. The swab was streaked onto nutrient agar plates and incubated at 37°C.

   b. Each student received a nutrient agar plate and a swab. Each student performed a swab culture of his or her teeth. The swab was streaked onto the agar plate. The plates were stored face down in the 37°C incubator and checked daily for growth. After 48 hours the plates were removed from the incubator, and each student recorded his or her results.

   c. Each student received a nutrient agar plate and a swab. Each student performed a swab culture of his or her teeth. The swab was streaked onto the agar plate. The plates were stored face down in the 37°C incubator and checked daily for growth. After 48 hours the plates were removed from the incubator, and each student counted the number of colonies present on the surface of the agar.

▲ Recording valid observations

As a part of your investigations, you will be asked to record observations on a skill sheet or in the results section of a lab report. There are different ways to record or display your observations.

1. **Short description:** Use descriptive words to explain what you did or saw. Write complete sentences. Give as much detail as possible about the experiment. Try to answer the following questions: What? Where? When? Why? and How?

2. **Tables:** Tables are a good way to display collected data. Later, the data can be plotted on a graph. Be sure to include a title for the table, labels for the sets of data, and units for the values. Check values to make sure you have the correct number of significant digits.

Table I: U.S. penny mass by year

Year manufactured	1977	1978	1979	1980	1981	1982	1983	1984	1985
Mass (g)	3.0845	3.0921	3.0689	2.9915	3.0023	2.5188	2.5042	2.4883	2.5230

3. **Graphs and charts:** A graph or chart is a picture of your data. There are different kinds of graphs and charts: line graphs, trend charts, bar graphs, and pie graphs, for example. A line graph is shown below.

    Label the important parts of your graph. Give your graph a title. The *x*-axis and *y*-axis should have labels for the data, the units, and the value range.

    This line graph has a straight line through the data. Sometimes data does not fit a straight line. Often scientists plot data in a trend chart first to see how it looks. Check with your teacher if you are unsure how to display your data.

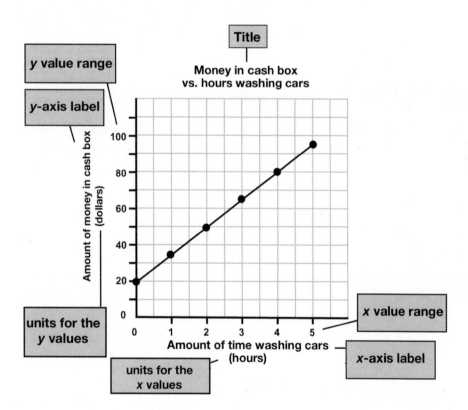

4. **Drawings:** Sometimes you will record observations by drawing a sketch of what you see. The example below shows what the student observed under a microscope.

Ulothrix

Each segment surrounded by clear tissue, cell wall

dark green quarters separated by clear zones

Nucleus "one cell"

400x

Many nearby strands

Colony grouping

Give the name of the specimen. Draw enough detail to make the sketch look realistic. Use color when possible. Identify parts of the object you were asked to observe. Provide the magnification or size of the image.

 ## Exercise 2: Practice recording valid observations

A lab report form has been given to you by your teacher. This exercise gives you a chance to read through an experiment and fill in the appropriate sections of the lab report form. Take this opportunity to practice writing and graphing scientific observations. Then answer the questions about the experiment.

A student notices that when he presses several pennies in a pressed penny machine, his brand new penny has some copper color missing and he can see silver-like material underneath. He wonders, "Are some pennies made differently than others?" The student has a theory that not all U.S. pennies are made the same. He thinks that if pennies are made differently now, he might be able to find out when the change occurred. He decides to collect a U.S. penny for each year from 1977 to the present, record the date, and take its mass. The student records the data in a table and creates a graph plotting U.S. penny mass vs. year. Table 2 shows some of his data:

Table 2: U.S. penny mass by year

Year manufactured	1977	1978	1979	1980	1981	1982	1983	1984	1985
Mass (g)	3.0845	3.0921	3.0689	2.9915	3.0023	2.5188	2.5042	2.4883	2.5230

 ## Analyzing and interpreting data

a. What observation did the student make *before* he began his experiment?

b. How did the student display his observations?

c. In what section of the lab report did you show observations?

d. What method did you use to display the observations? Explain your choice.

Why Keep an Engineering Design Log?

People who are trying to meet a need or solve a problem often follow an approach called the engineering cycle. The engineering cycle divides the design process into a series of stages that can be repeated as needed. Engineers often use a design log to keep track of their work. As you develop your own designs, keep a log to describe your ideas, gather information, ask questions, sketch plans, record results, and share findings. Your log should include the following stages:

1. Identify a Need

What problem are you trying to solve? What process are you trying to improve?

2. Research

Part of research is identifying what you know about a topic or closely related topics that may help you to design your solution. Then you may think about any additional information you need to gather and where you can find that information. What do you know about this topic? What additional information do you need?

3. Specify Requirements

The requirements of a design process include criteria, constraints, and trade-offs. Criteria are the standards a product or process must meet in order to be successful. Constraints are rules that limit the design of your product and include cost, availability of materials, and time. A trade-off is a compromise that exchanges one idea with another that may not be as good but still achieves the design requirements. For this design challenge, what are the design criteria and constraints? Can you identify any trade-offs at this stage? (Trade-offs often become more apparent during subsequent stages of the design process.)

4. Brainstorm Solutions

Describe the different ways you could solve the problem. Which solution should you explore first? Can you make a plan or blueprint of your solution?

5. Prototype

Now that you have chosen a solution, build your prototype. At this stage, you may need to gather some materials and/or tools. Did you learn something new as you constructed your prototype?

6. Test and Refine

How will you test your design and what data will you record? Once you have your prototype and other materials set up and you are ready to record your observations, conduct your tests. Construct a data table to record and analyze your data. Considering the results of your tests, what improvements should you make to your design?

7. Communicate

Scientists and engineers share their ideas within communities so that others may benefit from their work and review their conclusions. How will you share your design with others? What suggestions do others have for your design?

8. Reflect and Revise

The design process does not have to end when the results are communicated. What new information could you find that would help your design? Is there another type of test you could perform on your design, or an idea you weren't able to investigate in the first round of the process? Review your notes and reflect on these questions.

The engineering cycle can also be thought of as a series of decisions. This diagram shows where these decisions are often made.

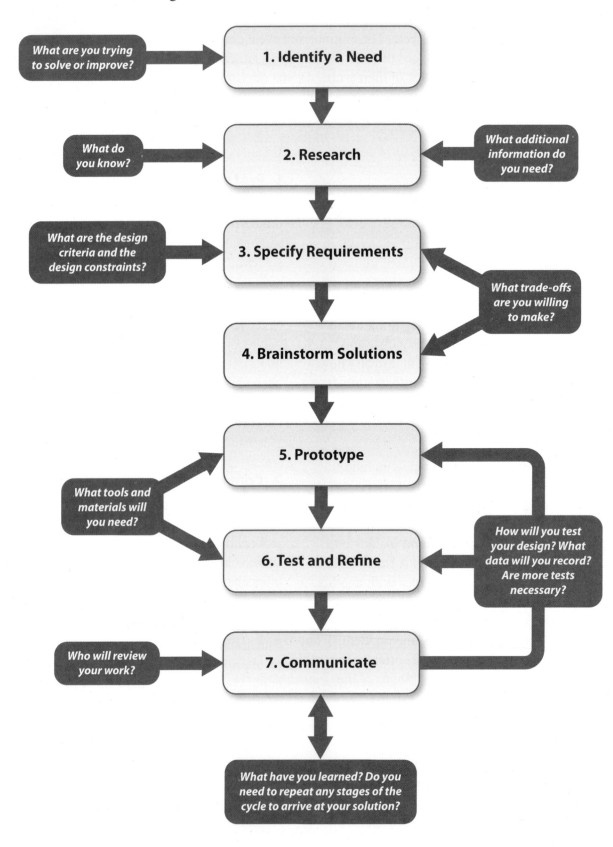

1. Identify a Need

What problem are you trying to solve?
What process are you trying to improve?

IDENTIFY
A NEED

_____

_____

_____

_____

_____

_____

_____

_____

_____

_____

_____

2. Research

Part of research is identifying what you know about a topic or closely related topics that may help you to design your solution. Then you may think about any additional information you need to gather and where you can find that information. What do you know about this topic? What additional information do you need?

_____

_____

_____

_____

_____

_____

_____

_____

_____

_____

3. Specify Requirements

The requirements of a design process include criteria, constraints, and trade-offs. Criteria are the standards a product or process must meet in order to be successful. Constraints are rules that limit the design of your product and include cost, availability of materials, and time. A trade-off is a compromise that exchanges one idea with another that may not be as good but still achieves the design requirements. For this design challenge, what are the design criteria and constraints? Can you identify any trade-offs at this stage? (Trade-offs often become more apparent during subsequent stages of the design process.)

4. Brainstorm Solutions

Describe the different ways you could solve the problem. Which solution should you explore first? Can you make a plan or blueprint of your solution?

_____

_____

_____

_____

_____

_____

_____

_____

_____

_____

_____

_____

5. Prototype

Now that you have chosen a solution, build your prototype. At this stage, you may need to gather some materials and/or tools. Did you learn something new as you constructed your prototype?

_____

_____

_____

_____

_____

_____

_____

_____

_____

_____

6. Test and Refine

How will you test your design and what data will you record? Once you have your prototype and other materials set up and you are ready to record your observations, conduct your tests. Construct a data table to record and analyze your data. Considering the results of your tests, what improvements should you make to your design?

_____

_____

_____

_____

_____

_____

_____

_____

_____

7. Communicate

Scientists and engineers share their ideas within communities so that others may benefit from their work and review their conclusions. How will you share your design with others? What suggestions do others have for your design?

8. Reflect and Revise

The design process does not have to end when the results are communicated. What new information could you find that would help your design? Is there another type of test you could perform on your design, or an idea you weren't able to investigate in the first round of the process? Review your notes and reflect on these questions.

_____

_____

_____

_____

_____

_____

_____

_____

_____

_____

Engineering Design Log Sample Grading Rubric

Stages of the Engineering Cycle	Exceeds expectations	Meets expectations	Does not meet expectations
Research and Specify Requirements	• Problem statement identifies needs • Statement of design requirements includes **at least 3** constraints and **at least 3** criteria	• Problem statement identifies needs • Statement of design requirements includes some constraints and criteria	• The problem statement is incomplete or the statement of design requirements does not include criteria and/or constraints
Brainstorm and Prototype	• Includes a diagram or plan of the prototype that indicates each of the design elements and their purpose or function	• Includes design elements indicated by a diagram or plan	• Does not include design elements indicated by a diagram or plan
Test and Refine	• The data table indicates which design was tested (ex. "1, 2, etc.") and the performance of each prototype • The data table lists trade-offs in each design • Accompanying the data table are diagrams of each design. Each diagram labels refinements made on the pervious design.	• The data table indicates which design was tested (ex. "1, 2, etc.") and the performance of each prototype • The data table lists trade-offs in each prototype	• The data table does not indicate which design was tested or the performance of that design • The data table does not list the trade-offs in each prototype • OR, a data table is not included